YORK NOTES

KS2 ENGLISH SATS

GRAMMAR, PUNCTUATION AND SPELLING TARGETED SKILLS & TEST PRACTICE

YEAR 5

ELIZABETH WALTER AND KATE WOODFORD

YORK PRESS
322 Old Brompton Road, London SW5 9JH

PEARSON EDUCATION LIMITED
Edinburgh Gate, Harlow,
Essex CM20 2JE, United Kingdom
Associated companies, branches and representatives throughout the
world

First published 2018

10 9 8 7 6 5 4 3 2 1

ISBN 978–1–2922–3286–7

Typeset by Carnegie Book Production
Printed in Slovakia

Image credits: lemmling/Open Clip Art for pages 5 and 98 / Shokunin/Open Clip Art for page 6 / Lorelyn Medina/Shutterstock for page 6 / Ilex/Open Clip Art for page 7 / Anon/allfree-clipart for page 7 / OCAL/clker for page 8 / Ana Angelova/Shutterstock for page 8 / OCAL/clkr for page 9 / stockakia/ Shutterstock for page 10 / Flipser/Shutterstock for page 11 / Klara Viskova/Shutterstock for page 12 / Muga/Open Clip Art for page 13 bottom / Ariros/ Shutterstock for page 14 bottom / StockSmartStart/Shutterstock for page 15 / OCAL/clkr for page 15 bottom / Zubada/Shutterstock for page 16 top / Yusak_P/Shutterstock for page 16 middle / Inkscapeforum.it/Open Clip Art for page 17 bottom / Alena Che/Shutterstock for page 18 bottom / peart/Shutterstock for page 19 bottom / Mirek2/Open Clip Art for page 20 bottom / Gammillian/Open Clip Art for page 20 bottom / marrishuanna/ Shutterstock for page 23 bottom / Terdpong/Shutterstock for page 24 middle / Yayayoyo/Shutterstock for page 24 middle / Maike Hildebrandt/ Shutterstock for page 24 bottom / ghrzuzudu/Shutterstock for page 25 middle / Amrides/Shutterstock for page 25 middle / Swanyland/Shutterstock for page 25 bottom / Schade/Open Clip Art for page 26 middle / skylark art/Shutterstock for page 26 bottom / Photoroyalty/Shutterstock for page 27 middle / Dominik Hladik/Shutterstock for page 28 middle / Iconic Bestiary/Shutterstock for page 28 bottom / Inky2010/Open Clip Art for page 30 top / NICK/clkr for page 31 bottom / OKhristy/Shutterstock for page 33 bottom / Rvector/Shutterstock for page 34 top / Ildar Galeev/Shutterstock for page 34 middle / Natallia Paslauskaya/Shutterstock for page 34 bottom / Stocklifemax/Shutterstock for page 38 bottom / Steinar/Shutterstock for page 39 top / Visual Generation/Shutterstock for page 39 bottom / Antikwar/Shutterstock for page 40 bottom / Lisa Kolbasa/Shutterstock for page 40 middle / graphic-line/Shutterstock for page 41 middle / Chaiwut Siriphithakwong/Shutterstock for page 41 bottom / Lukiyanova Natalia frenta/Shutterstock for page 42 middle / Amalga/Shutterstock for page 42 bottom / SunshineVector/Shutterstock for page 43 / graphic-line/Shutterstock for page 44 bottom / venimo/Shutterstock for page 47 / VectorPot/Shutterstock for page 48 / arbit/Shutterstock for page 48 bottom / oreshcka/Shutterstock for page 49 / Visual Generation/Shutterstock for page 52 middle / Karkas/Shutterstock for page 53 / Fun Way Illustration/Shutterstock for page 54 bottom / Treetops Interactive/Shutterstock for page 55 top / tarubumi/Shutterstock for page 55 bottom / Eganova Antonina/Shutterstock for page 56 bottom / Natykach Nataliia/Shutterstock for page 58 bottom / Spreadthesign/Shutterstock for page 60 top / Ellen McAuslan/Shutterstock for page 61 bottom / lescinqailes/Open Clip Art for page 64 bottom / Refluo/Shutterstock for page 64 bottom / Gorelova/Shutterstock for page 68 bottom / Lana__Samcorp/Shutterstock for page 69 bottom / Iconic Bestiary/Shutterstock for page 70 top / Lorelyn Medina/Shutterstock for page 70 bottom / Tarikdiz/Shutterstock for page 72 middle / Iconic Bestiary/Shutterstock for page 72 bottom / spline_x/Shutterstock for page 73 middle / Adem Demir/Shutterstock for page 73 bottom / Macrovector/Shutterstock for page 75 bottom / Art Alex/Shutterstock for page 76 middle / HappyPictures/ Shutterstock for page 77 bottom / Krylovochka/Shutterstock for page 78 bottom / zsooofija/Shutterstock for page 79 middle / Visual Generation/ Shutterstock for page 80 bottom / Visual Generation/Shutterstock for page 81 middle / YourElechka/Shutterstock for page 82 middle / Puwadol Jaturawutthichai/Shutterstock for page 84 bottom / Yayayoyo/Shutterstock for page 86 bottom / tynyuk/Shutterstock for page 87 bottom / Sim Lev/ Shutterstock for page 89 middle / John T Takai/Shutterstock for 89 middle / art-sonik/Shutterstock for page 90 middle / Yga/Shutterstock for page 90 middle / Pretty Vectors/Shutterstock for page 90 middle / LuckyVector/Shutterstock for page 90 middle / BlueRingMedia/Shutterstock for page 90 bottom / Viktorija Reuta/Shutterstock for page 91 bottom / Margaret Wilson/Shutterstock for page 92 bottom / Dualororua/Shutterstock for page 93 middle / Dark ink/Shutterstock for page 93 bottom / julietthai/Shutterstock for page 94 middle / Studio_G/Shutterstock for page 94 bottom / TheCreativeMill/Shutterstock for page 95 bottom / VectorShow/Shutterstock for page 96 bottom /

CONTENTS

HOW TO USE THIS BOOK

This bright and colourful workbook has been written to help you test your Grammar, Punctuation and Spelling knowledge, up to and including Year 5. Work through the tasks, practise the key skills you need to improve, and start preparing for the test!

There are lots of ways you can use this book, but let us keep it simple!

If you know a **particular skill** or **area** you struggle with …

❶ **LOOK UP** the page or section (e.g. 'Apostrophes') you need in the Contents.

❷ **TURN** to that page or section.

❸ **READ** the **information box** with a yellow background carefully at least twice.

❹ **WORK THROUGH** the numbered tasks.

❺ **CHECK your answers** by looking in the back of the book.

❻ How did you do? **TICK** one of the **'Got it/Try again/Ask an adult'** boxes. If you need to 'Ask an adult' for help, it could be a parent or other member of your family, or a teacher.

❼ When you feel ready, have a go at the **SATs PRACTICE** section at the end of each section. This will give you an even better idea of how you are getting on and help you prepare for the test. Then check your answers on that too.

If you would prefer to **work through the book a section at a time**, that is fine too! Put some time aside for each section (or just a number of pages). Then, follow stages 3–6 above.

Good luck!

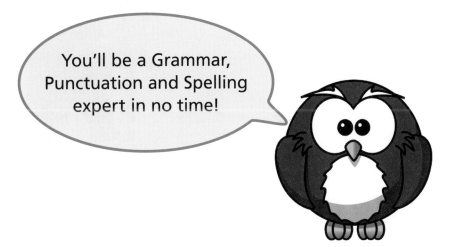

You'll be a Grammar, Punctuation and Spelling expert in no time!

Common nouns are words for any type of **person** ('boy', 'girl'), **place** ('castle') or **thing** ('ball', 'cat'). There are other types of nouns too:

Proper nouns (begin with **capital letter**)	Collective nouns (groups of people or animals)	Concrete nouns (things that really exist)	Abstract nouns (emotions and ideas)
Ben	team	table	fear
London	herd	hat	friendship

We use **noun phrases** to **add information** about **nouns** (for example, *a very high mountain, a really cool bike*).

1 Read the noun lists. **Circle** the correct type of **noun** (in brackets). There are two in each list.

a) laptop apple bravery trust   (concrete nouns)

b) city Paris desk Daniel   (proper nouns)

c) pen cat Sophia Spain   (common nouns)

d) flock bar cup bunch   (collective nouns)

e) table happiness truth skateboard   (abstract nouns)

2 **Underline** the **noun phrases** in these sentences.

a) Johnny has a smart, black scooter.

b) Mrs Taylor is a really good teacher.

c) A pack of wolves roams the forest.

d) We have an extremely grumpy old dog.

e) A very excited little boy ran up to me.

ADJECTIVES

Adjectives are used to **describe people and things**. They can be simple words, such as 'funny' and 'heavy', or they can be **more unusual words**, such as 'humorous' and 'weighty'.

Adjectives sometimes go before a noun. They can also appear later in a sentence, after the words 'is', 'are', 'was' or 'were'. You can make adjectives by adding **suffixes** to nouns and verbs – for example, 'wonder**ful**' and 'temp**ting**'.

1 **Underline** the adjectives in these sentences.

a) I had a delicious bowl of pasta.

b) Finn found the experience terrifying.

c) Your bag is so much smaller than mine.

2 Draw a line to **match** each word to the correct **suffix** to make an **adjective**.

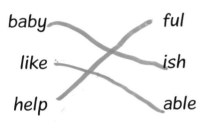

baby   ful

like   ish

help   able

3 **Complete** the text with adjectives and suffixes from the box.

striking   less   ful   cuddly   strong

Of all the animals that we saw, the lions were my favourite. They looked

so ...striking... with their muscular back legs, and yet so grace...ful...........

at the same time. And their faces were really ...strong........ – I've never seen

more beautiful animals. The guinea pigs were also sweet and ...cuddly... I

couldn't imagine how guinea pigs could survive in the wild. They looked so

help...less........ with their short little legs.

Got it!    Try again   Ask an adult

PRONOUNS

Pronouns are words we use to **replace** nouns. **Personal pronouns** are words such as 'I', 'me', 'they' and 'them'. We use these so we don't have to **repeat** the names of people and things.

A **possessive pronoun** is a word that shows who **owns** something – for example, 'mine', 'yours', 'hers', 'ours'.

1 **Match** these sentence beginnings to their correct endings. Draw lines between them. The first one has been done for you.

Sam took my book and he hasn't given — he's given it up.

We left a message for Sophie but — it back yet.

George and Ethan go to tennis club and — she hasn't replied.

My brother used to have guitar lessons but — we loved him.

Klara and I saw him in concert and — they really enjoy it.

2 **Underline** the personal pronouns in the sentences above.

3 **Rewrite** these sentences using pronouns to avoid repetition.

a) I asked Mrs Black for some help but Mrs Black was too busy.

I asked Mrs Black for some help but *she was too busy* .

b) My aunt and uncle came but my aunt and uncle couldn't stay.

My aunt and uncle came but *they couldn't stay* .

c) Millie and I gave some cakes to the younger children and the younger children loved the cakes.

Millie and I gave some cakes to the younger children and *they all loved the cakes* .

d) My mum told my brother to come home but my brother ignored my mum.

My mum told my brother to come home but ....

....

4 Put the following **pronouns** into the **correct column** of the table.

theirs   he   they   hers   we   ours   mine   you   his

Personal pronouns	Possessive pronouns
they we theirs	*mine his you ours he hers*

5 **Tick** the correct box to show if the underlined words in these sentences are personal pronouns or possessive pronouns.

	Personal pronoun	Possessive pronoun
a) <u>I</u> love dancing.	✓	✓
b) Isabel doesn't eat pizza. <u>She</u> doesn't like the cheese.		✓
c) The bike belongs to William but the scooter is <u>mine</u>.		✓
d) I invited Tom and Jack but <u>they</u> can't come.	✓	
e) Daisy, is this bag <u>yours</u>?		✓
f) Their house is a lot bigger than <u>ours</u>.		✓

I am yours

6 **Complete the sentences** with phrases that include a personal pronoun, a possessive pronoun or both. Use pronouns from the table in Question 4. The first one has been done for you.

a) Adam's family don't have a tent so ...*we lent them ours*....... .

b) My sister was ill so ....

c) Rosa and Grace were late so ....

d) My brother and I don't like pizza so ....

e) I'd forgotten my calculator so Jamie ....

Got it! ☀ ▢   Try again 🔍 ▢   Ask an adult ❓ ▢

9

A **relative pronoun** is a word such as 'which', 'that' or 'who', that **joins** two parts of a sentence with **related information**:

These are scarves. My sister knitted them.

These are the scarves <u>that</u> my sister knitted.

Use	Relative pronoun	Examples
for people	who/that	the waiter who brought the food the waiter that brought the food
for things and animals	which/that	the dog which went missing the dog that went missing
for places	where	the park where I used to play
for times	when	the time when she slipped on the ice
to say who something belongs to	whose	the boy whose sister was on TV

❶ Circle the correct **relative pronoun** in each sentence.

a) We visited the park [where / which] we used to play together.

b) Are those the girls [who / what] went to your school?

c) That's the woman [which / whose] daughter won the dance competition.

d) This is the game [who / that] Charlotte bought for me.

❷ Tick the sentence that contains a **relative pronoun**.

a) I told Alice I'd called her, <u>which</u> was the truth. ✓

b) The blue bowl is <u>yours</u>. ☐

c) Is <u>he</u> coming to your party? ☐

Got it! ☀ ✓   Try again 🔍 ☐   Ask an adult ❓ ☐

DETERMINERS

Determiners go before nouns. They give you **information about the noun**.
Some determiners say **which person or thing** you are talking about ('the', 'this', 'those'):

the dragon, *this* dragon, *those* dragons, *your* dragons ...

Other determiners say **how many or how much** you mean ('some', 'enough', 'twenty'). Another group shows who something belongs to ('my', 'your', 'his', 'their'). Some determiners are less specific ('a', 'an').

1 **Underline** the **determiners** in these sentences.

a) *My grandmother had five sisters and two brothers.*

b) *Those T-shirts are really cool but these ones are cheaper.*

c) *My aunt bought me a sweater with a picture of an apple on it.*

d) *His mum gave us a picnic and some money.*

e) *The people who lost their dog found him down a hole in a field.*

2 **Choose** a **determiner** from the box and write it in the correct sentence below. Use each determiner only once.

> the   a   an

a) *Olivia's uncle is .... author.*

b) *He's written .... book on the Arctic.*

c) *It's .... longest book I've ever seen.*

VERBS

Verbs are **doing, being or having words**. They say whether someone is eating, laughing or sleeping. They also tell you if water drips or flows.

<u>Are</u> you there, Oscar?

I <u>decorated</u> the cake.

Verbs also tell you **when something happened**. They have **different forms**, called tenses, which show when an action took place.

Tense	Example
Past	I did
Present	I do
Future	I will do

If **he, she or it** does something, the verb has an 's' on the end of it. If **I, you, we or they** do something, the verb does not have an 's'. When these rules are followed, we say **subjects** and **verbs agree**.

Poppy and Ava <u>play</u> tennis.

I <u>like</u> maths.

Emily <u>plays</u> football.

Thomas <u>likes</u> reading.

---

❶ **Underline** the verb in each sentence.

a) Thieves <u>stole</u> the necklace.

b) We hammered on the door.

c) It poured with rain for two whole days.

d) I really love my new art class.

❷ **Tick** the correct box to show if the verb in each sentence is in the past, present or future tense.

	Past	Present	Future
a) I <u>decided</u> not to go to buy the game.			
b) I <u>will hand in</u> my homework tomorrow.			
c) We usually <u>visit</u> my grandparents in the holidays.			
d) They <u>went</u> to Australia last summer.			

12

3 **Circle** the correct form of each **verb**.

a) We usually [takes / take] the path by the stream.

b) Alfie and Leo [were / was] at the cinema too.

c) Ella's teacher [is / are] going to give her some extra help.

d) My little sister [eat / eats] way more than me!

4 **Complete** the sentences with the correct form of the **verbs** in brackets.

a) I've already ~~did~~ my homework.   (do)

b) We ~~got the~~ the ball to the park and played football.   (take)

c) Last summer we ~~went~~ to Spain for our holidays.   (go)

d) When I was seven, I ~~went to~~ a skating party.   (have)

5 **Rewrite** the sentences so that the **verb** matches the **subject** in the sentence starter below each one. The first one has been done for you.

a) My best friend does karate classes at the weekend.

   I do karate classes at the weekend.

b) Harry and Remi are crazy about football.

   I ....

c) I have swimming lessons on Saturday.

   She ....

d) We like to make our own sushi.

   He ....

Got it! ☀ ▢   Try again 🔍 ▢   Ask an adult ❓ ▢

13

ADVERBS

Adverbs are often words that **give information** about **verbs**. They tell you **how** someone or something does something. Generally, adverbs are made up of the adjective plus the letters 'ly' on the end. An adverb can come before the <u>verb</u> that it tells you about or later in the sentence:

She <u>placed</u> the necklace carefully in its box.

I quickly <u>left</u> the room.

Adverbs also come before **adjectives**. For example, words such as 'really', 'very', 'so' and 'quite' are adverbs. They make the meaning of the <u>adjective</u> weaker or stronger:

I'm really <u>hungry</u>!

My dad's quite <u>tall</u>.

There are also **adverbs of possibility** – for example, 'definitely', 'probably', 'possibly', 'certainly', 'maybe' and 'perhaps'. We use these to say **how sure** we are about something. 'Perhaps' and 'maybe' often go at the beginning of a sentence. 'Certainly', 'definitely', 'probably' and 'possibly' often go before the main verb:

Perhaps we'll have time to call in on Joshua.

He'll probably refuse to come.

---

① **Underline** the adverb in each sentence.

a) I accidentally knocked the glass over.

b) Perhaps Lily would like to come.

c) She quickly lost interest in the subject.

d) He's very excited today.

e) She reluctantly agreed to come.

f) I'll certainly help you if I can.

g) I definitely put the book back after I'd finished with it.

2 **Tick** the box to show whether the underlined adverbs in these sentences modify an adjective or a verb.

	Adjective	Verb
a) Both boys behaved <u>badly</u>.	☐	☐
b) Mia is <u>very</u> excited about her birthday.	☐	☐
c) The food in the café was <u>extremely</u> expensive.	☐	☐
d) Jessica <u>carefully</u> unwrapped the present.	☐	☐
e) Josh gobbled the food up <u>hungrily</u>.	☐	☐

3 **Choose** the most suitable adverb from the box to fill each gap.

> suitably   suddenly   slowly   incredibly   quite

a) She's very old now, so she walks very ....

b) It's cold and wet out there, so make sure you dress ....

c) ...., without any warning, she shouted out, 'No!'

d) He's .... tall, but not huge.

e) I've never seen anyone so thin. He's .... slim!

4 **Complete** these sentences with your own ideas. The first one has been done for you.

a) This evening, *I will probably read a book.*

b) I will definitely .... when I'm older.

c) Maybe I will .... this weekend.

d) Perhaps I will .... next year.

e) I'll possibly .... tomorrow.

5 **Complete** these sentences with your own **adverbs**.

a) *He drives very* .... *.*

b) *This is important, so please listen* .... *.*

c) *I can do these sums really* .... *.*

d) *Alex can jump* .... *high.*

e) *You ate that doughnut* .... *quickly!*

6 **Write** three sentences, each containing **one** of these **adverbs**.

| easily | quite | definitely | secretly | possibly | very | quickly |

a) ....

....

....

b) ....

....

....

c) ....

....

....

Got it! ☀ ▢   Try again 🔍 ▢   Ask an adult ❓ ▢

ADVERBIALS

An **adverbial** is a word or a group of words that **does what an adverb does**. It may give information about **where** something happens, **how** it happens or **when** it happens:

Elizabeth ran <u>down the street</u>.

He spoke <u>calmly, without emotion</u>.

Adverbials can be used to **link ideas in different sentences**:

She hid in the bushes, hoping the creature would not see her. <u>Nearby</u>, an owl screeched.

Homework is sometimes hard to fit in during the evening. <u>However</u>, it is important.

They are also used to **link ideas in different** paragraphs:

Exhausted, Jacob went home.

<u>Later that day</u>, Oliver wondered where his friend had got to.

A fronted adverbial is a word or phrase **at the start of a sentence** that tells you about things like **place or time**. Generally, we put a comma after a fronted adverbial:

<u>In the background</u>, she could see her parents laughing.

<u>Earlier that morning</u>, I'd spoken to Alice and Ruby.

---

1 **Underline** the adverbials in these sentences.

a) *Leo and I see each other once a week.*

b) *Mum and Amelia spoke in hushed voices.*

c) *Max had forgotten to wear a watch. Consequently, he was late.*

d) *I'm meeting Harry in five minutes.*

❷ Draw a line to **match** the sentence starter on the left with the most suitable adverbial on the right.

Hurry, Alfie! The film starts   until her plate was empty.

Mala ate   peacefully.

She closed her eyes and slept   from time to time.

I still see him   in two minutes!

❸ **Write** a comma after the fronted adverbials in these sentences.

a) As fast as my legs could carry me I ran from the house.

b) All night long the wind whistled and the wolves howled.

c) Under the boughs of the old yew tree we sheltered from the rain.

d) Without a moment's hesitation she replied.

e) Before I start could you all switch off your mobile phones?

❹ **Complete** the sentences below with your own adverbials or fronted adverbials.

a) The old woman climbed the stairs ....

b) I go swimming ....

c) Pedro and I waited ....

d) Walking is free and it's good exercise. ...., it takes up a lot of time.

e) I tried and tried to get Jessica to come. ...., I just gave up.

Got it! ☀ ▢   Try again 🔍 ▢   Ask an adult ❓ ▢

18

PREPOSITIONS

A **preposition** is a short word that comes before a **noun** or **pronoun**. It links that noun or pronoun to another part of the sentence.

Prepositions of place are words such as 'up', 'down', 'in', 'out' and 'above'. Often, they tell us:

- **Where** something is in relation to the noun/pronoun

- The **direction** in which something is moving

> *The spoons are <u>in</u> that drawer.*

> *We both dashed <u>down</u> the stairs.*

> *Maria was <u>with</u> him when he fell.*

Prepositions of time are words such as 'before', 'after', 'during' and 'until'. They give information about **when** or **for how long** something happens:

> *We have fish and chips <u>after</u> swimming.*

> *I waited <u>until</u> he called.*

Prepositions of cause are phrases such as 'because of' and 'due to'. They tell us **why** something happened:

> *The buildings were closed <u>because of</u> the flooding.*

> *She missed a lot of school <u>due to</u> ill health.*

1 **Underline** the prepositions in these sentences.

a) *We're heading towards London.*

b) *I put my trainers on before going for a run.*

c) *The school was closed because of staff shortages.*

d) *We got there after you.*

e) *We didn't eat until nine o'clock.*

19

2 **Complete** each sentence with a suitable **preposition** from the box.

> on   under   down   with   towards   up   behind

a) *I set the plates down .... the table.*

b) *It was raining so we sheltered .... a tree.*

c) *She broke her ankle after she fell .... a flight of stairs.*

d) *Why don't you stay .... me and keep me company?*

3 **Underline** the **prepositions** in this paragraph. There are **seven** in total.

We both crawled into the cave, first me, then Jess. Inside the cave it was dark and damp. Water splashed on our heads. I could hear Jess breathing heavily behind me. I found my torch and pressed down the switch, but it wouldn't work. Perhaps the batteries were flat. Slowly my eyes started to adjust, and I began to make out vague shapes, just beyond my reach. Suddenly a strange rumbling sound came from below us, and we both jumped!

4 **Complete** the sentences so that each one contains a **preposition**.

a) *When I saw Isabel, she was walking ....*

b) *I put my bag ....*

5 **Describe** where to find things in your classroom using a range of **prepositions**.

The whiteboard is ....

... .

The door is ....

...

... .

> Got it! ☀ ▢   Try again 🔎 ▢   Ask an adult ❓ ▢

SATs PRACTICE

❶ Underline the **abstract noun** in each sentence below. (There is one in each sentence.)

I didn't want to spoil my friendship with Amy.

Sadly, the singer's childhood was not especially happy.

People often feel great love for their pets.

❷ Tick the sentence below that contains the correct form of the **superlative adjective**.

Tick **one**.

It's the most beautifulest sunset I've ever seen. ☐

It's the most beautiful sunset I've ever seen. ☐

It's the beautifulest sunset I've ever seen. ☑

❸ Complete the sentences below by writing the **determiners** from the box in the correct place. Use each determiner only once.

the   an   a

We saw ....*an*....... elephant.

It was ....*an*....... wild elephant.

It was ....*an*....... most enormous animal I've ever seen.

❹ Insert one **comma** in the correct place in the sentence below.

In the morning we'll go swimming.

❺ Underline the **pronouns** in the sentence below.

Jack and Archie called round and they brought me a present for my birthday.

❻ Tick one box in each row to show whether the underlined **adverb** describes a verb, an adjective or an adverb.

Sentence	Verb	Adjective	Adverb
It was <u>so</u> hot in the classroom today!			
Millie spoke <u>clearly</u>.			
She won <u>very</u> easily.			

❼ Draw a line to match each underlined word to its correct **word class**. Use each word class only **once**.

Sentence	Word class

Sentence   Word class

Dad was really <u>furious</u>.   pronoun

The racket is <u>mine</u>.   adverb

I'll <u>possibly</u> see you on Saturday.   determiner

<u>Those</u> milkshakes look so good!   adjective

Statements are sentences that **tell us things**. They start with a capital letter and end with a full stop:

Mia is tired.

The building at the top of the hill is a prison.

We use exclamations to show **strong feelings**. They start with 'How' or 'What' and end with an exclamation mark:

How beautiful this painting is!

What a terrible smell!

We use questions to **get information**. All questions end with a question mark. You can turn a statement into a question by adding a question tag like 'isn't it?' or 'don't they?':

Are you ready?

This cake is delicious, isn't it?

Commands tell people what to do. Urgent commands end with an **exclamation mark**. Less urgent ones end with a **full stop**:

Get out of the way!

Hang your coats up.

---

1 **Write** a full stop, question mark or exclamation mark at the end of each sentence.

a) *What an enormous house you have*

b) *How do you open this window*

c) *Elephants come from Africa and Asia*

d) *Run for your lives*

e) *Jason is very sporty, isn't he*

Got it!    Try again 🔎 ☐   Ask an adult ❓ ☐

23

PHRASES AND CLAUSES

A **phrase** is a **group of words** within a sentence. A phrase **doesn't have a** verb or it **doesn't have a subject** (sometimes it doesn't have either):

under the sink

a smelly old sock

put my phone away

Clauses are **parts** of sentences.

A **main clause** has a subject and a verb. It makes sense on its own:

The kitten played ...

A **subordinate clause** gives **extra detail**. It doesn't make sense on its own. Subordinate clauses can go at the **beginning** or at the **end** of the sentence:

Because he was clumsy, Dev broke the laptop.

Dev broke the laptop because he was clumsy.

❶ **Tick** the groups of words that are **phrases**.

a) *I ate hot sticky toffee!* ☐

b) *juicy cucumber* ☐

c) *a scary giant centipede* ☐

d) *going to the shops* ☐

e) *I made a terrible mistake.* ☐

❷ **Underline** the **main clauses** in these sentences.

a) *Jo overslept on Monday because she had been to a party.*

b) *Although it was raining, Saj didn't wear a coat.*

c) *Even if it is a silly game, Marge will play.*

d) *The plants won't grow unless it rains.*

e) *When he saw the homework, Ronnie sighed to himself.*

❸ Draw lines to **match** these **main** and **subordinate clauses**.

Even when the match is rubbish,   before preparing the salad.

She washed her hands thoroughly   don't put your hand up.

Although I love sci-fi,   I love going to see City play.

Our dog is slow and grumpy   detective films are great too.

Unless you know the answer,   even though he is still young.

❹ **Underline** the **subordinate clauses** in the sentence above.

❺ **Write** a sentence containing a **main clause** and a **subordinate clause**. Base it on the pictures and use the word in the middle:

.... before

....

❻ **Complete** the sentences by adding your own **clauses** to the end. The first one has been done for you.

a) You should leave ..*after the final whistle has blown.*..

b) Umar explained to Daisy that ....

....

c) Ice-creams make a mess even if ....

....

d) You will never beat me unless ....

....

Got it! ☀ ☐   Try again 🔍 ☐   Ask an adult ❓ ☐

RELATIVE CLAUSES

Relative clauses are parts of sentences that give **extra information** about **nouns**. We often use them to say **exactly which person or thing** we are talking about. Relative clauses start with **relative pronouns** such as 'that', 'who', 'which', 'where', 'when' or 'whose':

This is the house <u>where I was born</u>.

The woman, <u>who was very strong</u>, helped me carry the box.

If the noun with the relative clause isn't the **subject** of the **clause**, you can leave out the relative pronoun:

Did you see the cake that he brought?

Did you see the cake he brought?

TIP! Here, 'he' is the subject, not 'the cake'.

1 **Underline** the relative clause in each sentence.

a) We went to a theme park, which was fantastic!

b) The man, whose name was Daniel Khan, was a dentist.

c) Where is the pen that I lent you?

d) The house in London, where I lived with my parents, was tiny.

e) I gave my old bike to Lexie, who was very pleased with it.

2 **Underline** the relative pronoun in each sentence.

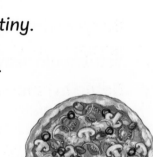

a) The pizza that I chose was a vegetarian one.

b) We went to the Van Gogh museum, which is in Amsterdam.

c) That's the woman who shouted at me.

d) Do you remember the time when we got lost?

e) That's the place where my granddad was born.

❸ Circle the correct **relative pronoun** in each sentence.

a) *Is she the woman [what / which / who] stole your money?*

b) *We're having my favourite meal, [which / that / who] is chicken.*

c) *The holiday [whose / what / that] I enjoyed most was in Spain.*

❹ Draw lines to **match** the **main clauses** and the **relative clauses**.

She showed me the cupboard	*when Dad lost his passport.*
She's the lady	*which unlocks the back door.*
That was the time	*whose car broke down.*
This is the key	*where they keep the pens and paper.*

❺ Tick the sentences where it is possible to leave out the **relative pronoun**.

a) *This is the ring that I found.*

b) *Have you seen the painting which Lottie did?*

c) *That's the dog that bit me.*

❻ Write relative clauses to complete each sentence, using the words in brackets and any other words you need.

a) *Do you remember the day* ....

....?

(Sofia / dropped / phone / river)

b) *I'd like to see the letter* ....

....

(Grandpa / wrote / when / in the army)

c) *She gave me some medicine* ....

....

(made / cough / much better)

Got it! ☀ ❏   Try again 🔍 ❏   Ask an adult ❓ ❏

FORMING SENTENCES

A **simple sentence** is made of just **one** main clause:

I walk to school.

A **compound sentence** has **two or more main clauses** joined together:

<u>*I walk to school*</u>, but <u>*my friend Harvey catches the bus*</u>.

A **complex sentence** has a **main clause and a** subordinate clause:

<u>*Harvey catches the bus to school,*</u> <u>*although it's less than a mile from*</u>
<u>*his house.*</u>

❶ **Identify** the **sentence type** and **tick** the correct box.

a) *It was dark, so I took a torch.*

   simple ☐   compound ☐   complex ☐

b) *Seb wants to go to the seaside today.*

   simple ☐   compound ☐   complex ☐

c) *You won't pass your test unless you work harder.*

   simple ☐   compound ☐   complex ☐

d) *The tickets were expensive, but the show wasn't very good.*

   simple ☐   compound ☐   complex ☐

❷ Draw lines to **match** the sentence halves.

Ella can't play football	*we won't be able to take everyone.*
Although he doesn't speak French,	*if I get a good school report.*
Unless we get a bigger car,	*even though it rained all day.*
Dad says he'll take me out for a pizza	*because she's broken her leg.*
We had a great time at the seaside	*he had a wonderful time in Paris.*

28

❸ Tick the sentences where the order of the **clauses** could be changed.

a) *If you don't understand the question, ask your teacher.* ☐

b) *I wanted to go shopping, but it was too late.* ☐

c) *Unless we leave now, we won't get there in time.* ☐

d) *I knew the answer to all the questions, and so did Katie.* ☐

❹ Complete complex sentences based on these **simple sentences**.

a) *Dad was tired. He still played football with us.*

Even though ....

....

b) *I was eating my tea. The phone rang.*

While ....

....

c) *Our visitors were late. They got lost.*

....

because ....

❺ Use your **own ideas** to complete each sentence. The **sentence type** is shown in brackets.

a) *Freya is really good on the drums* ....

.... (compound)

b) *My school is* ....

.... (simple)

c) *If you want to make friends,* ....

.... (complex)

Got it! ☀ ☐   Try again 🔍 ☐   Ask an adult ❓ ☐

CO-ORDINATING CONJUNCTIONS

Co-ordinating conjunctions join two main clauses together to make a compound sentence. The most important ones are 'and', 'or', 'but' and 'so':

I had my dinner __and__ then I watched TV.

I like running __but__ I'm not keen on team sports.

1 **Underline** the co-ordinating conjunctions in these sentences.

a) It was a hot summer's day and the sun was shining.

b) It was getting dark, so we decided to go inside.

c) You can come with us now or you can meet us later.

2 **Complete** the sentences using co-ordinating conjunctions from the box.

and   or   but   so

a) I wanted to buy the game, ... it was too expensive.

b) The door opened .... the president walked in.

c) My rabbit was ill .... I took him to the vet.

d) It's possible to go by bus .... to take a train.

3 Use co-ordinating conjunctions to **link** these simple sentences.

a) Shall we watch TV? Shall we listen to music?

....

b) I sing in a choir. I play drums in a band.

....

c) I saw a thief. I called the police.

....

Got it! ☀ ❑   Try again 🔎 ❑   Ask an adult ❓ ❑

SUBORDINATING CONJUNCTIONS

> **Subordinating conjunctions** join a **main clause** to a **subordinate clause**. They can go at the **beginning** or **in the middle** of a sentence.
>
> 'When', 'while', 'if', 'because', 'although' and 'unless' are common subordinating conjunctions:
>
> Alia was late <u>because</u> she missed her bus.
>
> <u>Because</u> she missed her bus, Alia was late.
>
> **TIP!** If the subordinate clause comes first, you need a **comma** before the main clause.

1 **Circle** the correct **subordinating conjunction** to complete each sentence.

a) *We'll be late [although / while / unless] we hurry up.*

b) *[Because / Although / If] Maddy was ill, she didn't go to school.*

c) *[Unless / Because / While] we were walking to school, we saw a car accident.*

d) *I won't buy the tickets [unless / if / although] they're very expensive.*

2 **Draw lines** to make sentences of three parts.

I learned to speak German	*because*	*you feel chilly.*
Eva ate her spinach	*when*	*our car broke down.*
You can put your coat on	*if*	*we lived in Berlin.*
We were late	*even though*	*she didn't like it much.*

Got it! ☀ ▢   Try again 🔍 ▢   Ask an adult ❓ ▢

CONNECTING SENTENCES AND PARAGRAPHS

We use **cohesive devices** to connect sentences and **paragraphs**. They help writing flow and show the relationship between ideas. They can be single words or **phrases**, and they usually come at the beginning of a sentence:

Roads are closed because of heavy snowfall. Therefore, there is no school today.

Tourists make our city very crowded. On the other hand, they are good for local businesses.

1 **Circle** the best **cohesive device** to link each pair of sentences.

a) *I had to go back for my passport. [Nevertheless / Consequently / Finally], I was late.*

b) *I was worried that my friend would be angry that I forgot her birthday. [However / In addition / Therefore], she didn't mind at all.*

c) *I can tell you how to make the best chocolate cake. [More importantly / In fact / Firstly], you need to beat some butter and sugar together.*

d) *We didn't know why Martina wasn't at the party. [As a result / Later on / Moreover], we heard that she had argued with the host.*

2 **Match** the sentences. **Write** the number of the second sentences (1–5) after the first sentences (a–e).

a) *I find this city too crowded. ....*

b) *We worked hard all day to do the cleaning. ....*

c) *Playing football is really fun. ....*

d) *All the trains were cancelled. ....*

e) *I'm getting a new phone next week. ....*

1) *Finally, we managed to finish it all.*

2) *Therefore, we couldn't go to London.*

3) *Meanwhile, I have to put up with this old one.*

4) *On the other hand, there's a lot to do here.*

5) *More importantly, it keeps me fit.*

Got it! ☀ ⬜   Try again 🔍 ⬜   Ask an adult ❓ ⬜

People often use **non-standard English** when they are speaking, but you need to make sure that you use **standard English** for your school work. Here are some rules for using standard English:

- The **subject** of a sentence must **agree** with the **verb**. That simply means that you need to use the **correct form of the verb** (for example, 'he <u>was</u>', 'we <u>were</u>').

- 'Them' is a **pronoun**. It **replaces** a **noun**, so it can never be used in front of a noun (for example, 'I ate the sweets' becomes 'I ate them' not 'I ate them sweets').

- Words like 'haven't', 'no', 'don't', 'not' and 'never' are **negative** words. You should **only use one** of them in a **clause**.

- When you use **modal verbs** like 'would', 'could' or 'must' in a past **tense**, remember to write 'have' after them, not 'of'. For example, 'I should have worn a coat', never 'I should of worn a coat'.

❶ Circle the correct form of the **verb** in each example.

a) I think she [do / does] understand you.

b) We saw a fox when we [was / were] in the wood.

c) Ruby and Poppy [goes / go] to school with me.

d) I don't think our teacher [was / were] very pleased.

❷ Tick the sentences that use **determiners** correctly.

a) I want some of them sweets.

b) Those cakes are delicious.

c) I've got some new shoes. I really like them.

d) Could you pass me them books, please?

3 **Circle** the correct words in these **negative** statements.

a) I haven't got [any / no] money.

b) There [was / wasn't] no food left.

c) She didn't give us [no / any] advice.

d) There [were / weren't] no people in the building.

4 **Tick** the box to show if the **past forms** in these sentences are correct or incorrect.

	Correct	Incorrect
a) I <u>done</u> all my homework yesterday.		
b) My brother's <u>taken</u> my football.		
c) I've already <u>spoke</u> to the teacher about it.		
d) I <u>seen</u> the movie last week.		
e) Ben has <u>drawn</u> a picture of a fish.		

5 **Tick** the sentences that are written in correct **standard English**.

a) He can't have eaten all those cakes.

b) I think you should of apologised.

c) We went inside because we was cold.

d) She hasn't got any friends.

e) You could of taken Ricky with you.

Got it! ☀ ☐   Try again 🔍 ☐   Ask an adult ❓ ☐

34

SATs PRACTICE

❶ Draw a line to match the clauses.

We won't need the umbrella	you can borrow this one.
If you need an umbrella,	because it's raining.
You should take an umbrella	unless it rains.

❷ Tick the sentence that must end with a question mark.

Tick **one**.

I don't know why Beth isn't here ☐

It's cold in here, isn't it ☐

What a wonderful view ☐

He showed me how to use the camera ☐

❸ Which sentence is a compound sentence?

Tick **one**.

Lou carried on working even though she was tired. ☐

I listened to the album, but I didn't like it. ☐

He offered me a cup of tea and a piece of cake. ☐

You mustn't go in the kitchen or the bathroom. ☐

❹ Tick one box in each row to show whether the underlined clause is a **main clause** or a **subordinate clause**.

Sentence	Main clause	Subordinate clause
We left home <u>as soon as everyone was ready</u>.		
Although she's young, <u>she's not very fit</u>.		
<u>Because Emma's quite shy</u>, she didn't want to come to the party.		

❺ Draw a line to match each sentence to the correct **conjunction**. Use each conjunction only **once**.

	Sentence	Conjunction

It was a hot day .... we didn't need our coats.

or

I ate the soup .... I didn't like it very much.

so

Shall we play chess .... shall we go swimming?

although

❻ Which option correctly completes the **sentence** below?

That's the man .... hat blew off in the wind.

Tick one.

that ☐

who ☐

which ☐

whose ☐

7 Draw a line to match each sentence to its correct **function**.

Sentence	Function
How cold it is tonight!	statement
Open your books on page 17.	question
Our house has three bedrooms.	exclamation
Where is the railway station?	command

8 Tick one box in each row to show whether the sentence is written in **standard English** or **non-standard English**.

Sentence	Standard English	Non-standard English
Could we use some of those pencils, please?		
I haven't got no brothers or sisters.		
I met Mia when we was both in Year 2.		
You should have asked the teacher for help.		

9 Circle the **subordinating conjunction** in this sentence.

While our parents were busy, my brother and I did some painting and watched TV.

10 Rewrite the sentence below so that it is in **standard English**.

I think you could of tried harder.

....

PART THREE: VERB FORMS AND TENSES
SIMPLE PAST AND SIMPLE PRESENT

We use the **simple present tense** for things that happen **now**, especially **regular events** or situations and states that **do not change**:

My dad <u>works</u> in a shop.

The washing machine <u>is</u> in the kitchen.

We use the **simple past** for things that **happened at a particular time** in the past. It is usually formed by adding 'd' or 'ed' to the main **verb**. However, many common verbs have **irregular** past simple forms:

regular

We <u>walked</u> up the hill.

Someone <u>stole</u> my bike.

irregular

1 **Tick** the boxes to show if these sentences are in the **simple present** or the **simple past** tense.

	Present	Past
a) We went to Croatia on holiday.		
b) Alvin felt rather sad.		
c) We always have fish and chips on Fridays.		
d) Ali and Ben walked to school.		
e) Our house is near the river.		

2 **Circle** the correct form of the **verb** in these sentences.

a) My parents [payed / paid] me for washing the car.

b) We [hidden / hid] behind a tree.

c) Hannah [swam / swum] fifty lengths.

d) We [stayed / staid] in a nice hotel.

❸ **Tick** the sentences that use the correct form of the **simple past**.

a) *We slept in bunk beds.* ☐

b) *She said she was sorry.* ☐

c) *We found some money in the street.* ☐

d) *My brother hitted me.* ☐

❹ **Write** the **simple past** form of these verbs.

a) *hope* ....

b) *throw* ....

c) *work* ....

d) *drive* ....

e) *fly* ....

f) *write* ....

❺ **Rewrite** these sentences with **simple past** verbs.

a) *Alex goes to school by bus.* ....

b) *We grow lots of vegetables.* ....

c) *I tell her all my news.* ....

d) *I know Peter.* ....

❻ **Write** one sentence using the **simple present** and one using the **simple past** to describe what is happening in this picture.

The man .... (simple present)

The man .... (simple past)

Got it! ☐   Try again 🔍 ☐   Ask an adult ❓ ☐

VERBS IN THE PERFECT FORM

We use the **present perfect tense** for things that **happened in the past**, especially with words like 'just', 'already', 'ever', 'never' and 'yet'.

It is formed by using 'have' (with 'I', 'you', 'we', 'they') or 'has' (with 'he', 'she', 'it') and a past tense verb:

Lucas has invited me to his party. I have never been to his house before.

We use the **past perfect** to talk about things that happened **before** the events we are talking about now. It is formed by using 'had' (often shortened to 'd) and a past tense verb:

I knew that Tegan had read the letter. I had seen her open it.

Past tense **verbs** used in the perfect form are usually formed by adding 'd' or 'ed' to the main verb. However, many common verbs do not follow this pattern (for example, 'swim/swam/swum', 'hide/hid/hidden').

❶ **Complete** each of these sentences with the correct **past tense** verb from the box.

> finished   met   swollen   been

a) *I twisted my ankle and it has .... up.*

b) *The show had .... by the time we arrived.*

c) *Had your brother .... to Germany before?*

d) *My sister has a new boyfriend, but I haven't .... him yet.*

❷ **Complete** these perfect sentences with **'has'**, **'have'**, **'hasn't'** or **'haven't'**.

a) *Amber .... done her homework yet.*

b) *My friends .... made me a birthday cake.*

c) *I .... been to New York, but I really want to!*

d) *.. you visited your aunty recently?*

❸ Complete the sentences using the **perfect** form of the verbs in brackets.

a) Mum's .... away my old coat because it was ripped. (throw)

b) Anna hasn't .... tennis for a long time. (play)

c) I've .... the apples in a bowl. (put)

❹ Find and correct one mistake in the **tenses** in each sentence. Cross out the mistake and write the correct word on the line.

a) A thief has stole my bike. ....

b) Lucas had runned all the way. ....

c) Have you ever sleeped in a tent? ....

d) The dog had bited her arm. ....

❺ Complete the sentences using the correct form of the **verbs** in the box. Remember to add the correct form of the verb 'to have' before the past tense verb. The first one has been done for you.

> drink   ~~break~~   meet   feed

a) The x-ray showed that I ....._had broken_.... my arm.

b) .... you .... the cat today?

c) Oh no! Someone ....
all the milk.

d) I was sure that I .... the
woman before.

PRESENT AND PAST PROGRESSIVE

We use the **present progressive tense** to talk about things that are **happening right now**. Use the correct form of the **verb** 'be' followed by another verb ending with 'ing':

Marta is doing her homework at the moment. Her parents are trying to help her.

We use the **past progressive** to talk about things that were **happening over a period of time in the past**. Use 'was' or 'were' followed by another verb ending with 'ing':

The boys were playing football. An old man was watching them.

❶ Circle the correct form of the **verb** in each example.

a) We [was / were] going to London.

b) Lois and Petra [is / are] having their dinner.

c) [Was / Were] you expecting to see Damia?

d) I [am / is] reading a really good book.

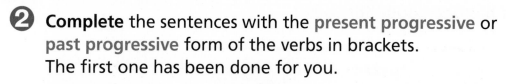

❷ Complete the sentences with the **present progressive** or **past progressive** form of the verbs in brackets. The first one has been done for you.

a) Please be quiet. I ......*am trying*...... to read. (try)

b) Dan learned French while he .... in Paris. (work)

c) Jade couldn't hear me because she .... to some loud music. (listen)

d) I'll call the children. They .... outside at the moment. (play)

Got it!  ▢   Try again 🔍 ▢   Ask an adult ❓ ▢

MODAL VERBS

We use **modal verbs** **with other verbs** – for example, to show whether something is **possible**, **allowed**, **likely**, **certain** or **necessary**. The modal verbs are 'can', 'could', 'will', 'would', 'must', 'should', 'ought', 'shall', 'might' and 'may':

Martina <u>can</u> speak Russian.

We <u>mustn't</u> talk too loudly.

Modal verbs can be **used with different tenses**:

| simple present |

We <u>could</u> smell the fresh bread.

We <u>could</u> have smelled the fresh bread.

| present perfect |

Make sure you **spell modal verbs correctly** – especially their contracted **negative** forms:

can ➜ can't	should ➜ shouldn't
could ➜ couldn't	will ➜ won't
might ➜ mightn't	would ➜ wouldn't
must ➜ mustn't	shall ➜ shan't

❶ **Tick** the sentences that contain a **modal verb**.

a) *I don't know how to ride a horse.*

b) *Sasha might be moving to Mexico.*

c) *Rick won't play tennis with me.*

d) *We haven't got any fruit.*

❷ **Circle** the most suitable **modal verb** in each sentence.

a) *I'm not sure if Emma [might / can / should] hear us.*

b) *It looks as if it [must / can / might] rain later.*

c) *If you have to get up early, you [couldn't / wouldn't / shouldn't] be late to bed.*

d) *I don't think I [would / must / might] ever try bungee jumping.*

3 **Circle** the correct **modal verb** in each sentence.

a) I was annoyed because Millie [mustn't / wouldn't] lend me a pen.

b) Ben ran off before I [could / can] tell him.

c) Please give this letter to your Mum or Dad. It's very important, so you [mustn't / don't] lose it.

4 **Complete** these sentences with a **modal verb** from the box.

> mustn't   couldn't   should   might

a) We .... go away for Christmas but we're not sure yet.

b) If someone is bullying you at school, you .... tell a teacher.

c) The coach leaves at nine o'clock and it won't wait for anyone, so you really .... be late!

d) Unfortunately, I .... go to the party because I was ill.

5 **Write** the sentences so that they mean the **opposite**. The first one has been done for you.

a) You should go to Mia's party.

You shouldn't go to Mia's party.

b) Tennis would be a good sport for you.

....

c) Pablo won't help us.

....

d) You must eat all the food.

....

> Got it! ☀ ▢   Try again 🔎 ▢   Ask an adult ❓ ▢

44

SATs PRACTICE

❶ Which sentence uses the **past perfect** form?

Tick **one**.

I didn't know you had lost my number. ☐

I think I have forgotten my keys. ☐

Ben had a new bike for his birthday. ☐

I was telling Rosie about our holiday. ☐

❷ Underline the **modal verbs** in the sentences below.

I can't play the guitar.

Everyone in the school must wear the school uniform.

You shouldn't go swimming straight after a meal.

❸ Circle the two words that show the **tense** in the sentence below.

I met Mason at the sports centre and we went swimming together.

❹ Which option correctly completes the sentence below?

I'm not sure whether Mum .... my bike yet.

Tick **one**.

have fixed ☐

was fixing ☐

has fixed ☐

had fixed ☐

❺ Tick one box in each row to show if the sentence is in the **past simple** or **past progressive**.

Sentence	Past simple	Past progressive
The children were getting on the coach.		
We all sat on the floor.		
Brandon was eating his dinner.		

❻ Which sentence shows that you are **most likely** to win the competition?

Tick **one**.

I must win the competition. ⬜

I might win the competition. ⬜

I will win the competition. ⬜

I should win the competition. ⬜

❼ Complete the sentences below using the **present progressive form** of the verbs in the boxes.

We need to be quiet. Dad ....
in the next room.

work

My sisters .... some cakes for
tea.

make

46

You must use a **capital letter** at the beginning of **every sentence**. This means that when you finish one sentence and start another, you have to write a capital letter **every single time**, even if the words seem unimportant (for example, 'a' or 'if'):

An aeroplane flew above them.

Is the laptop switched on?

When you write the word 'I' to talk about yourself, you must **always** use a capital letter, even in the middle of a sentence:

I will write to them when I have more time.

You also need capital letters for **proper nouns** such as names of people, places, months and days of the week:

On Sunday, we are going to London to see a Shakespeare play at the Globe Theatre.

You must use **full stops** at the end of **statements** and **commands**:

That is an oak tree.

Stir the mixture gently.

1 **Tick** the words that should have **capital letters**.

paris ☐   tuesday ☐   umbrella ☐

chimney ☐   david ☐   october ☐

2 **Tick** the boxes to show if the **capital letters** and **full stops** are correct or incorrect in these sentences.

		Correct	Incorrect
a)	*Jamie and Rory are going to london on saturday.*	☐	☐
b)	*Romeo and Juliet is a play by William Shakespeare.*	☐	☐
c)	*We need to buy Eggs, Butter and Flour*	☐	☐

Got it! ☐   Try again ☐   Ask an adult ☐

QUESTION MARKS AND EXCLAMATION MARKS

You must write a question mark ? at the end of every question. Questions often start with **question words** such as 'why', 'where' or 'how', but they can also start with other words:

Is it time to go?

Some statements contain question words, but they **don't need question marks**:

He <u>asked</u> if I was warm enough.

Exclamation marks ! are used for exclamations, which begin with 'How' or 'What':

What a pretty picture!

We also use them for urgent commands and to show strong feelings:

Look out!

He fell flat on his face!

1 **Number** the parts to put these sentences in the correct order. Write a question mark or an exclamation mark at the end of each one. The first one has been done for you.

	4	2	1	3
a)	that was!	/ delicious	/ what a	/ meal

b) bring a / do I / coat / need to / why

c) those / gave you / who / sweets

d) immediately / the building / you must / leave

2 **Tick** the boxes to show whether these sentences should end with a question mark, an exclamation mark or a full stop.

		?	!	.
a)	Maria comes from Spain	☐	☐	☐
b)	How beautiful your garden looks	☐	☐	☐
c)	The movie was great, wasn't it	☐	☐	☐
d)	How long did you have to wait	☐	☐	☐

Got it! ☐   Try again ☐   Ask an adult ☐

We use **commas ,** to separate items in a **list**. The commas go **between each item except the last two**. Write 'and' or 'or' before the last item in the list. Do not include a comma before 'and' or 'or':

Inside the boxes we found letters, photographs, postcards and notebooks.

We also use commas for lists of **adjectives** and **verbs**:

My cat is soft, furry, friendly and lazy.

All they did was eat, talk, sleep and read.

Commas can help to **make your meaning clear**:

For lunch we had cheese, pies, tomatoes and bread.
('cheese' and 'pies' are two different items)

For lunch we had cheese pies, tomatoes and bread. ('cheese pies' is one item)

1 How many items are there in each list? **Write** the number in the box.

a) *We had a hamper with fruit cake, chocolate, biscuits and lemonade.*

b) *We went to the supermarket and bought fruit, buns, meat pies, bananas and bread.*

c) *We made masks using paper plates, coloured string, scraps of felt and glitter.*

d) *The menu includes chicken curry, salad, ham omelettes and chips.*

2 **Write** commas in the correct places in these sentences.

a) *I gave cards to Mum Dad Kyle and Ben.*

b) *We spent the whole day polishing scrubbing dusting hoovering and cooking.*

c) *My next door neighbour is unfriendly rude noisy and bossy.*

d) *My favourite subjects are History Religious Studies French and English.*

❸ Tick the boxes to show if the use of **commas** is correct or incorrect in these sentences.

		Correct	Incorrect
a)	My hobbies are reading swimming, painting and horse riding.	☐	☐
b)	This jacket is available in red, brown, navy or green.	☐	☐
c)	I found the film long, and boring.	☐	☐
d)	At the zoo we saw lions, tigers, elephants and giraffes.	☐	☐

❹ Complete these lists with items from the box. Make sure you put **commas** in the correct places.

tomatoes	a torch	onions	oil	a sleeping bag	herbs	a water bottle

a) I'm going to make a pasta sauce. I need to buy ....

....

b) For our camping trip, I need to take ....

....

❺ Complete these sentences using your own ideas. Make sure you put **commas** in the correct places.

a) Jack's best friend is kind .... and generous.

b) In my grandparents' living room, they have a sofa ....
.... and a TV.

c) Arlo's really sporty. He's good at running ....
.... and gymnastics.

Got it! ☀ ☐   Try again 🔍 ☐   Ask an adult ❓ ☐

50

COMMAS 2

Never use a **comma** to join two sentences together. You must either have **two separate sentences** or **join them with a conjunction**.

I suddenly felt tired, I fell asleep. x

I suddenly felt tired. I fell asleep. ✓

I suddenly felt tired and I fell asleep. ✓

When joining sentences with a conjunction, you can add a comma before the conjunction if the two parts of the sentence make sense on their own:

Ollie loves maths, but Kai hates it.

1 **Tick** the boxes to show if the use of **commas** is correct or incorrect in these sentences.

		Correct	Incorrect
a)	*We were being noisy, so the teacher told us off.*	☐	☐
b)	*I like reading comics, and so does my friend Harry.*	☐	☐
c)	*I can't open the door, it's locked.*	☐	☐
d)	*I have a bike, I can't ride it.*	☐	☐

2 **Rewrite** these sentences correctly using a **conjunction**.

a) *I felt cold, I shut the window.*

....

b) *My brother fell over, he broke his leg.*

....

c) *I wanted a sandwich, we didn't have any bread.*

....

d) *I didn't eat the pizza, I don't like cheese.*

....

Got it! ☀ ☐   Try again 🔍 ☐   Ask an adult ❓ ☐

51

COMMAS 3

In a **complex sentence**, you need a comma after the subordinate clause **if it comes first**:

> If the bus doesn't come, we'll have to walk.

If the main clause comes first, you don't need a comma:

> We'll have to walk if the bus doesn't come.

You also need a comma after a fronted adverbial:

> Next to the armchair, there was a small table.

> However, the letter never arrived.

1 **Complete** the sentences with an **adverb** or **adverbial phrase** from the box. Add **commas** where they are needed.

> In the end   After school   In addition   Nevertheless

a) .... I hope to go to university.

b) We were all tired. .... we decided to continue our climb.

c) We weren't sure what to do. .... we decided to go home.

d) The hotel provides all meals. .... free drinks are available all day.

2 **Write** a **comma** in the correct box in each sentence.

a) Because ☐ the roads were icy ☐ Mum had ☐ to drive slowly.

b) If you are cold ☐ you can ☐ put ☐ the heating on.

c) Unless you feel ☐ better later ☐ you won't be able ☐ to go to the show.

d) Although ☐ Amber can't swim ☐ she still enjoys playing ☐ in the water.

3 **Change** the order of the **clauses**. Remember to use **commas** correctly. The first one has been done for you.

a) My uncle is very generous although he doesn't have much money.

Although he doesn't have much money, my uncle is very generous.

....

b) Your mum will be worried unless you call her.

....

....

c) We drew silly pictures when the teacher wasn't looking.

....

....

d) You can come with me if you want to.

....

....

4 **Tick** the box to show if the use of **commas** is correct or incorrect in these sentences.

		Correct	Incorrect
a)	*In a moment, you will hear the sound of bells.*	☐	☐
b)	*I read a book, while my brother did his piano practice.*	☐	☐
c)	*Even though it's old I really like this coat.*	☐	☐
d)	*You can go outside as soon as we've finished eating.*	☐	☐

You can use a pair of **commas** to **add extra information** to a sentence. They work in the same way as **brackets**. The sentence should **still make sense** if you take out the information between the commas:

My brother, who is six years old, loves video games.

My brother loves video games.

1 Write **commas** in the correct boxes in each sentence.

a) The train ☐ despite ☐ stopping several times ☐ arrived ☐ on time.

b) The city ☐ which attracts a lot ☐ of tourists ☐ is ☐ quite large.

c) The children ☐ even ☐ the older ones ☐ all enjoyed ☐ the circus.

d) My neighbour ☐ Mrs Ashton ☐ is ☐ a nurse at ☐ the local hospital.

2 Tick the boxes to show if the use of **commas** is correct or incorrect in these sentences.

	Correct	Incorrect
a) We went to Zadar, a historic town, for the day.	☐	☐
b) My friend, Luiz who is from Brazil loves football.	☐	☐
c) Everyone in my family, especially my sister, loves music.	☐	☐
d) Anne my Mum's friend, took me, to the theatre.	☐	☐

❸ Add commas to these sentences.

a) The cat whose name was Ginger let us stroke him.

b) We went to Miller's a music shop to buy a recorder.

c) Her hair which is very long is brown.

d) The meeting which is only two days away will be very important.

❹ Put the three parts of each sentence in order and add commas where they are needed.

a) I had to go and see the headteacher / in her office / Mrs White

....

....

b) to help you / Katya Smith / You should ask my friend

....

....

❺ Complete the sentences using one of the phrases from the box. Add commas where they are needed.

> my dad's boss
>
> which has over 100 members
>
> a small country in Asia

a) They visited Brunei .... last month.

b) Bill Fowler .... invited us to a barbecue.

c) The club .... meets every Saturday.

Got it! ☀ ⬛   Try again 🔍 ⬛   Ask an adult ❓ ⬛

BRACKETS AND DASHES

You can also use a pair of brackets (or dashes – to **add extra information** to a sentence. Adding extra information to a sentence using pairs of brackets, dashes or commas is called parenthesis. The sentence should **still make sense** if you take out the information between these punctuation marks:

Mr Jones (our maths teacher) drives a sports car.

When brackets come **at the end of the sentence**, write the **full stop** after the final bracket:

Ahmed was late for school (as usual).

When you use dashes in this way, **leave a space** on either side of them:

Fry the onion – in the large pan – for ten minutes.

1 **Write brackets in the correct boxes.**

a) *We had to ☐ take Fatma ☐ my cousin ☐ to the station ☐ .*

b) *We managed ☐ to find ☐ the cinema ☐ in the end ☐ .*

c) *We're having ☐ chicken curry ☐ which I love ☐ for dinner ☐ .*

d) *Everyone was happy ☐ except Annie ☐ who had ☐ a bad headache ☐ .*

2 **One dash in each sentence is in the wrong place. Circle the incorrect dash and underline the space where it should go.**

a) *Make sure you do your homework – all of it before – you go to bed.*

b) *Mr Tam one of the teachers – at my school – gave me this book.*

c) *He brought his luggage all – twelve suitcases of it – with him.*

d) *Go and pick some tomatoes – big ones – if you can for lunch.*

❸ One **bracket** or **dash** is missing from each sentence. **Write** it in the correct place.

a) *My parents are — I hope getting me a bike for my birthday.*

b) *Dexter Lee's brother) painted this picture.*

c) *Tickets (which are only £5 are available from the school office.*

d) *I enjoy playing cricket and other sports — at school.*

❹ **Complete** each sentence with a phrase from the box. Put a **dash** before and after the phrases.

> a village near Cambridge   the one with the sports car
> many of them children

a) *My uncle* .... *is coming to visit next week.*

b) *Five hundred people* .... *were at the event.*

c) *My mum lived in Stapleford* .... *for five years.*

❺ **Rewrite** these sentences to put them in the correct order. Add **brackets** around one part. Add a **capital letter** where needed.

a) *Cara Phipps / a bracelet / I gave my best friend*

....

b) *his latest movie / especially the special effects / I really enjoyed*

....

c) *the blue one / my dress / I wore*

....

d) *is my cousin / the one with black hair / that boy*

....

Got it! ☀ ▣   Try again 🔎 ▣   Ask an adult ❓ ▣

SPEECH PUNCTUATION

We use **inverted commas** '' (also called **speech marks**) when we write down **something that someone says**.

When the speech **comes first**, we use a **comma** (not a **full stop**), a **question mark** or an **exclamation mark** before the final inverted comma:

> 'You're late,' said Rupa.

> 'What's your name?' asked the woman.

When other words come before the speech, the comma goes **in front of** the inverted commas. The speech starts with a **capital letter**, even though it isn't at the beginning of the sentence:

> Shannon said, 'Let's go to the cinema.'

If he said or she said or Mandy said comes in the middle of the speech, the second part of the sentence **does not start with a capital letter**:

> 'This painting,' said Hugo, 'is worth over a million pounds.'

When you write a conversation, you need to **start a new line** every time a different person speaks.

Reported speech is when we use our **own words** to say what someone said. **Do not** use inverted commas for reported speech:

> Maddison said that she was hungry.

---

1 **Tick** the boxes to show if the **inverted commas** are correct or incorrect in these sentences.

		Correct	Incorrect
a)	'This is a lovely beach,' said Roxy.	☐	☐
b)	Dean cried, 'Look out'!	☐	☐
c)	'I don't understand, said Jenny, why you are so upset.'	☐	☐
d)	'Who's that man?' asked Sean. 'Do you know him?'	☐	☐

2 Tick the boxes to show whether these sentences should have inverted commas.

		Yes	No
a)	Becky said she was hungry.	☐	☐
b)	Alex muttered I'm so bored!	☐	☐
c)	Paul asked if we were OK.	☐	☐
d)	Laura told me that she had an idea.	☐	☐

3 **Circle** the punctuation mistakes in these sentences. Write the number of the mistake in the box.

> 1) missing inverted comma   2) comma in wrong place
> 3) needs a capital letter

a) 'I recognise you', said the man. 'We met at Marc's party.' ☐

b) Gavin asked, 'are you hungry?' ☐

c) 'I hope, said Izzie, 'that you will be happy here.' ☐

d) 'It's late,' said Dad. 'you should go to bed.' ☐

4 **Tick** the sentence in each pair that has the correct **punctuation**.

a) 'You never know,' said Fiona, 'what might happen next.' ☐

'You never know,' said Fiona 'What might happen next.' ☐

b) The police officer said, 'Stand back, please!' ☐

The police officer said, 'Stand back, please'! ☐

c) 'Hey, Beth!' said Zoe, 'how are you?' ☐

'Hey, Beth!' said Zoe, 'How are you?' ☐

d) 'Can you help me, please?' begged Arianna. ☐

'Can you help me, please'? Begged Arianna. ☐

59

❺ Write the correct **punctuation marks** in the gaps.

a) 'This is Mark ☐ ☐ said Summer. 'He's my brother ☐ ☐

b) 'I think ☐ ☐ whispered Lou ☐ ☐ that she likes us.'

c) 'Hey ☐ ☐ shouted Katie. 'What are you doing ☐ ☐

d) 'It's not a mouse ☐ ☐ said Georgie ☐ ☐ It's a rat.'

❻ Rewrite the sentences using the correct **speech punctuation**.

a) Is dinner ready asked Jan

....

b) The man yelled look out

....

c) I don't think said Adam that you should go there

....

❼ Write / at each point where this conversation should **start a new line**.

'I'm scared,' whispered Callum. 'It's too dark in here.' 'Don't be such a baby,' his sister replied. 'We'll be in trouble if Mum finds out,' Callum continued. 'She isn't going to find out,' his sister muttered, 'unless you tell her.'

❽ Rewrite each sentence so that it is written using reported speech. The first one has been done for you.

a) 'I'm tired,' complained Josh. .... *Josh complained that he was tired.* ....

b) Rosie said, 'The money is in the bank.'

....

c) 'I've lost my coat,' said Sami.

....

Got it! ☀ ☐   Try again 🔍 ☐   Ask an adult ❓ ☐

60

APOSTROPHES 1

Apostrophes ' are used for **contractions**. These are words such as can't and we've, where two words have been **joined together** with one or more letter missed out. The apostrophe **shows where those letters used to be**:

They'll be late.

We couldn't see the stage.

The contraction 'd can mean had or would.

The contracted form of will not is won't and the contracted form of cannot is can't:

will not ➔ *won't*

cannot ➔ *can't*

Make sure you know the difference between it's and its. It's means it is or it has:

It is raining ➔ *It's raining.*

It has stopped working ➔ *It's stopped working.*

Its means 'belonging to it':

The dog licked its paws.

❶ **Write out** the full form of these **contractions**.

a) *I'd* ....

b) *We'll* ....

c) *You've* ....

d) *I'm* ....

❷ **Complete** the **contractions** in these sentences using the verb in brackets.

a) *Where....................................... my pen? (is)*

b) *Do you think you... pass the test? (will)*

c) *Ryan can............................... ride a bike yet. (cannot)*

d) *I think I.. broken my leg. (have)*

❸ Write the **contracted form** of these words.

a) had not ....

d) should not ....

b) she would ....

e) he is ....

c) will not ....

f) cannot ....

❹ Complete the sentences with the **contracted form** of the words in brackets.

a) Peter .... lend me his pencil. (would not)

b) I thought .... read the book before. (she had)

c) My friends are still up in the mountains. I hope .... be OK. (they will)

d) I think .... right about this movie. (you are)

❺ Tick the boxes to show whether the use of **it's** and **its** is correct or incorrect in these sentences.

		Correct	**Incorrect**
a)	The baby has lost it's dummy.	☐	☐
b)	I broke the vase. It's going to be difficult to mend.	☐	☐
c)	Its a lovely day today.	☐	☐
d)	Our new car is great, but I don't like its colour.	☐	☐

❻ Complete the sentences with **it's** or **its**.

a) I found this ring – I think .... Marta's.

b) This jigsaw should be easy – .... pieces are quite big.

c) We can't call Kerry – .... the middle of the night.

d) I don't like this shirt because .... sleeves are too long.

Got it! ☀ ☐   Try again 🔍 ☐   Ask an adult ❓ ☐

APOSTROPHES 2

We use **apostrophes** to show **who something belongs to**. This is called **possession**. To show possession for a singular person, add 's:

Mia's bike is red.

James's dad is a builder.

We can say **what** something belongs to as well, though this is less common:

The fork's handle has broken.

For plural words ending in s, **add an apostrophe only**. For all other plurals, add 's:

The boys' changing room is over there.

She is in the women's team.

❶ **Underline** the words in these sentences that should have **apostrophes**.

a) *My friends stroked the cats soft fur.*

b) *Megans mum likes baking cookies.*

c) *We helped to carry Mrs Millers bags.*

❷ **Tick** the boxes to show if the use of **apostrophes** is correct or incorrect in these sentences.

		Correct	Incorrect
a)	*I enjoy watching womens' football.*	☐	☐
b)	*I met my brother's new girlfriend yesterday.*	☐	☐
c)	*I often stay at my grandparents' house on Saturdays.*	☐	☐

❸ **Write** a phrase that means the same as each phrase below, using a possessive **apostrophe**. The first one has been done for you.

a) the coat belonging to Sally   *Sally's coat* ....

b) the car belonging to my parents ....

c) the handle of the saucepan ....

d) the heat of the sun ....

4 **Complete** the sentences using the words with **apostrophes** from the box.

> friend's   friends'   elephant's   elephants'

a) I am going to borrow my .... bike.

b) We spoke to the .... owners.

c) He told us the .... name.

d) My dad can never remember my .... names.

5 **Find** one mistake connected with **apostrophes** in each sentence. Circle it and write the correct word on the line.

a) Ali's house is bigger than Farouks. ....

b) His teams' kit is red with white stripes. ....

c) My grandparents' house is bigger than Toms. ....

d) We had to tidy up Jane's childrens' toys. ....

6 **Add** apostrophes where they are needed in these sentences.

a) My sisters jumper is full of holes.

b) We had tomatoes and Mums home-made bread.

c) Someone had let down my bikes tyres.

d) The castles walls were very thick.

❶ Underline the words in this paragraph that need an **apostrophe for possession**.

Have you seen Rileys photos? He went to Mallorca, to stay in his familys apartment there. The beaches look awesome!

❷ Which sentence uses correct **speech punctuation**?

Tick **one**.

'Give that money to me'! Rob shouted. ☐

Julia whispered 'I'm scared.' ☐

'I know,' Kiera said 'That you're right.' ☐

'What time is it?' asked Yusuf. ☐

❸ You are helping a friend correct the punctuation in the sentence below. Which **two** pieces of advice should you give to correct the punctuation?

Although Reece is shy he is kind funny and helpful.

Tick **two**.

There should be a comma after 'shy'. ☐

There should be a comma between 'kind' and 'funny'. ☐

There should be a comma before 'and'. ☐

There should be a comma after 'Reece'. ☐

❹ Insert **brackets** in the correct places in the sentence below.

Mrs Botha my next-door neighbour is a train driver.

❺ Which sentence uses the **comma** correctly?

Tick **one**.

I really like Annie, she's a good friend. ☐

Our van is very old, so it doesn't go very fast. ☐

We live in Liverpool, that's in the north of the UK. ☐

This is my bike, it's new. ☐

❻ Tick the sentence that must end with an **exclamation mark**.

Tick **one**.

What an unusual building ☐

They have an extremely large garden ☐

All the cakes in this café are home-made ☐

I have no idea what to do ☐

❼ Replace the underlined words in the sentences below with their **expanded forms**.

You'll meet Joe on Sunday. He's great fun.

☐ _____   ☐ _____

I've known him for a long time.

☐ _____

❽ Tick two boxes where missing **commas** should go in this sentence.

I got ☐ a jigsaw ☐ puzzle ☐ a kite ☐ a football ☐ and some sweets ☐ for my birthday.

❾ Rearrange the words in the statement below to make it a **question**.
Use only the given words. Remember to punctuate your sentence correctly.

Statement: Anna is a dancer.

Question: ....

❿ Which sentence uses **commas** correctly to show extra information?

Tick **one**.

My brother who is a doctor, has a job, in Paris. ☐

My friends, apart from Shahena, all live in the city. ☐

We often, go to my aunty's, on the train. ☐

Laurie didn't give me, a birthday present, this year. ☐

⓫ Tick the option that needs **inverted commas**.

Tick **one**.

Sam said that he was bored. ☐

She admitted that she had stolen the money. ☐

This is fantastic, Bao said. ☐

Ariana told me she knew Steven. ☐

A **word family** is a group of words that all contain a part which is **the same** (or very similar). The part that all the **related words** share is the **root**. For example, the words below are a word family. They share the root 'auto-':

*auto*graph, *auto*biography, *auto*matic, *auto*-reply

The members of a word family are all **linked in meaning**, even when they refer to very different things.

*ped*estrian, *ped*al, ex*ped*ition, centi*ped*e ('ped' means 'foot')

*cent*imetre, per*cent*, *cent*ury, *cent*ipede ('cent' means 'a hundred')

*terr*ain, extra-*terr*estrial, *terr*itory ('terr' means earth or land)

❶ **Circle** the **root** shared by each word in these **word families**.

a) telephone, phonics, microphone

b) photograph, photocopy, photosynthesis

c) vacancy, vacuum, evacuate

d) biology, biodegradable, biodiesel

e) export, portable, transport, teleport

❷ **Write** the **word roots** from Question 1 next to their meanings below. The first one has been done for you.

a) light   *photo* ....

b) carry ....

c) life ....

d) sound ....

e) empty ....

 Got it! Try again  Ask an adult

68

PLURALS

A **plural** is **two or more** of something. To make most **nouns** plural, you just add '-s' to the end of the word. If the word ends in the letters 's', 'x', 'z', 'sh' or 'ch', you add '-es':

phone ➔ phones   box ➔ boxes

If a word ends in a **consonant** plus 'y' – for example 'country' – you make it plural by replacing the 'y' with 'i' and adding 'es' ('countr**ies**'):

fly ➔ flies   memory ➔ memories

Words that end in 'o' usually just have an 's' at the end when they are plural, but a few need 'es':

potato**es**   tomato**es**   hero**es**

To make a plural of a word that ends in 'f' or 'fe', you change the 'f' to 'v' and add 'es':

half ➔ halves   knife ➔ knives   leaf ➔ leaves

A few nouns ending in 'f' do not follow this rule. Their plural form just has an 's' on the end:

belief ➔ belie**fs**   chef ➔ che**fs**   reef ➔ ree**fs**   roof ➔ roo**fs**

A few words have a plural form that is the same as the word for one of them, including some words for animals:

lots of sheep   three deer   loads of fish   a herd of buffalo   several moose

---

1 **Tick** the correct **spelling** in each pair.

a) roofs ☐   rooves ☐

b) knives ☐   knifes ☐

c) foxs ☐   foxes ☐

d) sheep ☐   sheeps ☐

e) potatos ☐   potatoes ☐

2 **Complete** the **plural** forms of these nouns using '-s' or '-es'.

a) tomato..

b) table..

c) belief..

d) wish..

e) box..

3 **Complete** the gap in each sentence with the correct **plural** form of the noun in brackets.

a) My dad wanted to look around the old .... (church).

b) We saw some .... (deer) in the forest.

c) My mum must have at least twenty .... (scarf).

d) Have you eaten all the .... (cherry)?

e) I love kicking piles of autumn .... (leaf).

4 **Circle** the misspelt **plural** noun in each sentence. Write each plural noun correctly.

a) There were several plates of sandwichs. ....

b) We spied several mooses and even some wolves. ....

c) I have so many good memorys of those two holidays. ....

d) I've washed up the glasses but not the dishs. ....

e) Chefs use very sharp knifes. ....

Got it! ☀ ☐   Try again 🔍 ☐   Ask an adult ❓ ☐

PREFIXES 1

A **prefix** is a group of letters, such as 'un-', 'over-', 'under-', that is added to the **start of a word**. It changes the meaning of that word.

When we add a prefix to a word, the spelling of the original word (the **root word**) **stays the same**.

Here are some important prefixes:

de- means 'opposite' or 'take away' (for example, 'to declutter')

dis- means 'not' or 'opposite' (for example, 'to disagree', 'disbelief')

over- means 'too much' (for example, 'overconfident', 'to overeat')

mis- means 'not' or 'wrong' (for example, 'misbehaviour')

re- means 'again' (for example, 'to reheat', 'to reapply')

under- means 'too little' (for example, 'to underachieve')

❶ **Complete** these words with the correct **prefixes** from the box.

> dis   over   mis   re

a) *I wasn't very impressed with the food. It was a bit*
   ....*cooked.*

b) *That's one of the* ....*advantages of living in the country.*

c) *The match ended in a draw so they will have to* ....*play it.*

d) *Unfortunately, I think she* ....*understood my instructions.*

❷ Draw lines to **match** the two halves of these sentences containing **prefixes**.

I really dis	*heard what I said.*
The teacher told her to re	*paid for all that work she does.*
Sara is definitely under	*like having to get up in the dark.*
I think David mis	*write the whole essay.*

3 **Draw lines** from the **prefixes** to the words that they combine with. Then write the complete words underneath.

obey	over	crowded
appear	mis	read
honest	dis	spell

a) ....

b) ....

c) ....

d) ....

e) ....

f) ....

4 **Circle** the two **prefixes** in this sentence.

Jogging is how I de-stress when I'm feeling overworked.

5 **Add prefixes** to these words so that the sentences make sense.

a) *In my opinion, Hollywood actors are all ....paid.*

b) *If children ....behave in class, the teacher tells them off.*

c) *Isabel doesn't like the colour we painted her bedroom – I think we may have to ....paint it.*

d) *Anyone found breaking the rules will immediately be ....qualified from the competition.*

Some prefixes mean **'not' or 'opposite'** and combine with verbs and adjectives. The prefixes 'un-', 'in-', 'im-', 'il-', 'ir-' all make a word mean the opposite (for example, 'unhappy').

These prefixes have the same meaning. There are some rules for the prefixes that begin with 'i':

im- is used before words that begin with 'm', 'b' and 'p' (for example, 'impossible', 'immature')

il- is used before words that begin with 'l' (for example, 'illegal')

ir- is used before words that being with 'r' (for example, 'irregular')

in- is used before words that begin with other letters (for example, 'incorrect')

❶ **Write** these adjectives after the correct prefixes.

> usual   regular   credible   legal   mortal

a) *im*...

b) *in*...

c) *un*...

d) *ir*...

e) *il*...

❷ **Circle** the correct prefixes in these adjectives.

a) *in/im*patient

b) *in/un*visible

c) *im/in*complete

d) *un/in*accurate

e) *im/in*possible

❸ Complete these sentences with the correct word from the box. Then circle the **prefix** in each word.

> irregular   impatient   informal   unable   unbelievable

a) I've never seen anyone jump so high. It was ....!

b) You'll just have to wait a while. Don't be so ....!

c) Most verbs follow the usual rules of grammar but a few are ....

d) I wanted to contact her but was .... to reach her.

e) You shouldn't use .... language when you are writing essays.

❹ Underline the incorrect **prefix** in each sentence, then write it correctly.

a) It's unlegal not to use a car seat for a child. ....

b) I got home and depacked my bags. ....

c) We can't see this gas – it's imvisible. ....

d) It would be inpolite not to reply to their invitation. ....

❺ Write a sentence containing each of the words below.

a) inconsiderate

....

b) uneven

....

c) irresponsible

....

Got it! ☀ ▢   Try again 🔎 ▢   Ask an adult ❓ ▢

Prefixes add certain meanings to **root words**. Here are some useful prefixes with their meanings:

auto- has two meanings: **1)** 'done yourself' (for example, 'autobiography');
2) 'working without the help of people' (for example, 'auto-reply', 'automated')

sub- means 'under' or 'less' (for example, 'submarine' – under the sea)

super- means 'bigger or better than most' (for example, 'superhero')

❶ Complete these words with the correct **prefixes** from the box.

> super   sub   auto

a) *So how do you keep warm in ....-zero temperatures?*

b) *After the concert, I got the lead singer's ....graph.*

c) *I can't perform miracles — I'm not ....human!*

❷ Write a sentence that includes each of the words containing **prefixes** below.

a) *automatic*

....

....

b) *superhero*

....

....

Got it! ☐   Try again 🔎 ☐   Ask an adult ❓ ☐

HYPHENATING PREFIXES

Sometimes you will see a **hyphen** (-) between a **prefix** and a **root word**. This might be where two **vowels** are next to each other – for example, 'co-ordinate', or where there could be confusion with another word – for example, 're-cover' (which could be confused with 'recover'):

I'd like to <u>re-cover</u> that old chair.

It took Emily months to <u>recover</u> after the operation.

❶ **Underline** five words that might be written with a **hyphen** after the **prefix**.

reelect	retell	immortal	cooperate	proactive
unplug	reintroduce	reorder	incredible	illegal

❷ **Write** the five words from Question 1 with the **hyphen** in the correct place.

a) ....

b) ....

c) ....

d) ....

e) ....

❸ **Complete** these sentences with the correct spelling of each word with a **prefix**.

a) *represented* or *re-presented*?

She first .... her country at the Olympics aged just seventeen.

She was originally given the award last year and then .... with it at a later ceremony.

b) *resort* or *re-sort*?

I think I might .... those cupboards – I'm going to put all the pens in one place and the paper in another.

The shops were all closed so I had to .... to eating last week's stale bread!

c) *resent* or *re-sent*

I wasn't sure whether Ethan got my original email so I .... it.

I thought he might .... the fact that his brother got more money than him.

d) *recoiled* or *re-coiled*

We no longer needed the rope so I .... it neatly and left it in the garage.

She .... in horror at the sight of the wound.

e) *resign* or *re-sign*

After thirty years working for the same company, he's decided to ....

I was asked to .... the form in black ink this time.

4 **Complete** the sentences with the correct prefix from the box. Use a hyphen after the prefix. You will need to use one prefix twice.

re   co   pre

a) We hope very much that everyone will ....operate and we can all work together.

b) These animals died out in this region fifty years ago but were recently ....introduced.

c) It's a website that allows you to buy items that have been ....owned.

d) She was elected leader of the party four years ago and was ....elected last month.

Got it! ☀ ▢   Try again 🔎 ▢   Ask an adult ❓ ▢

77

SUFFIXES

A **suffix** is a group of letters that we add to the **end of a word**. It changes a word so that it **means something different** or **changes its** tense. It may also turn a word into **a different word class**. For example, a suffix may turn a noun into an adjective.

Some suffixes, such as '-ise', '-ify' and '-ate', change nouns and adjectives to verbs:

liquid + ise = liquidise

pure + ify = purify

active + ate = activate

Adding a suffix sometimes **changes the spelling** of the **root word**. For example, when a root word ends in 'e' and the suffix starts with a vowel, you drop the 'e' in the root word:

active ➜ activate

If a root word ends in the letters 'fer' and the 'fer' syllable is stressed when you add the suffix, **double the last letter** before the suffix:

refer ➜ referring/referred

TIP! If the 'fer' syllable is not stressed in the new word, do not double the last letter (for example, 'reference').

❶ **Circle** the words with **suffixes** that are spelt correctly.

a) *She scrawled her signature [messyly / messily] at the end of the letter.*

b) *Someone had [grabbed / grabed] her bag and run off with it.*

c) *I think we need to [simplify / simpleify] the instructions for the younger children.*

d) *Tom is always dropping and spilling things. I've never known such [clumsiness / clumsiness].*

e) *Emily [beged / begged] me to take her to the fair.*

❷ Add the **suffixes** (in brackets) to the word roots. Make any spelling changes that are necessary. The first one has been done for you.

a) *hungry (-ly)* ....*hungrily*..........

d) *prefer (-ed)* ....

b) *stop (-ed)* ....

e) *sit (-ing)* ....

c) *pretty (-ness)* ....

❸ Draw lines to **match** the word **roots** to the **suffixes**.

modern   –ate

class   –ise

acceler   –ify

❹ Complete the words in the sentences using the **suffixes** from the box.

> -ise   -ify   -ate

a) *I'd like to apolog............ for making so much noise last night.*

b) *I've decided to nomin............ Otis to represent our class.*

c) *We have to categor............ these foods according to their food group.*

d) *You can see these details when you magn............ the cells under a microscope.*

e) *I'm going to dedic............ this poem to my sister.*

❺ Draw lines to **match** the correct halves of these sentences containing words with **suffixes**.

In the poem, birds seem to symbol   *ate using clicks and whistles.*

These insects are easy to ident   *ise freedom.*

Dolphins continue to fascin   *ify with their red markings.*

They seem to communic   *ate us with their behaviour.*

WORDS ENDING IN 'TION', 'SION', 'SSION' AND 'CIAN'

Many **nouns** end in a 'shun' sound – for example, 'deci**sion**'. This 'shun' ending may be spelt four ways:

tion (for example, 'posi**tion**')

sion (for example, 'ver**sion**')

ssion (for example, 'discu**ssion**')

cian (for example, 'magi**cian**')

There are some general rules for these spellings. If the **root word** from which the noun comes ends in:

't' or 'te', the 'shun' sound is spelt '-tion' (hesitate ➔ hesitation)

'd', 'de' or 'se', the 'shun' sound is spelt '-sion' (divide ➔ division)

'ss' or 'mit', the 'shun' sound is spelt '-ssion' (transmit ➔ transmission)

'c' or 'cs', the 'shun' sound is spelt '-cian' (politics ➔ politician)

TIP! 'Suspicion' is the only frequent word that has 'cion' at the end, not 'cian'.

❶ **Underline** the correct ending to the **nouns** in these sentences. Use the **root words** in brackets to help you.

a) *My sister is doing a lot of revi**cion/sion** for her exams. (revise)*

b) *In which direc**tion/sion** did they go? (direct)*

c) *I need to do some calcula**sions/tions**. (calculate)*

d) *We had to call an electri**cian/sion** to fix the problem. (electric)*

e) *Jack does a really good impre**ssion/sion** of Mrs Baker. (impress)*

❷ Draw lines to **match** the start of the words with the endings below.

celebra   ssion

 musi   tion

 admi   sion

exten   cian

Root words: *celebrate, music, admit, extend*

3 **Complete** the words in these sentences with the correct ending. Use the root words in brackets to help you.

a) *I think you made a good deci*... . *(decide)*

b) *'St' is an abbrev*... *for 'street'. (abbreviate)*

c) *I have a confe*... *to make. (confess)*

d) *He's a famous politi*... . *(politics)*

e) *Both moves are anima*... . *(animate)*

4 **Complete** the crossword with nouns ending in **'tion'**, **'sion'**, **'ssion'** or **'cian'**, using these clues.

Across
1 one type of something, for example one form of a song
4 the opposite of subtraction
5 a talk with someone else
6 when you are very careful

Down
2 This person tests your eyes
3 A bomb causes this.

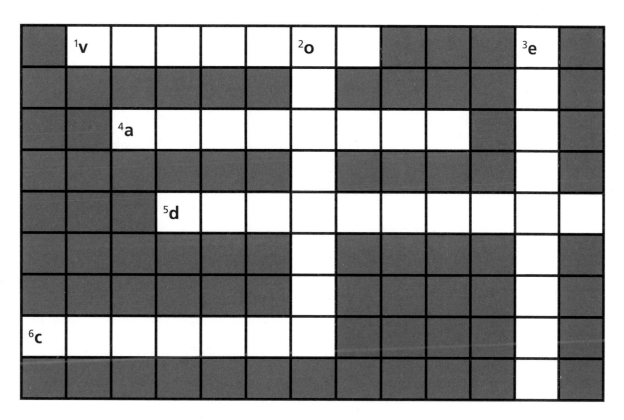

Got it! ☀ ▢   Try again 🔍 ▢   Ask an adult ❓ ▢

81

WORDS ENDING IN 'CIOUS' AND 'TIOUS'

Lots of **adjectives** end in a 'shus' sound – for example, 'deli**cious**'. This ending may be spelt 'cious' or 'tious'.

There are two general rules to help you with this:

1) If the **root word** ends in 'tion' (for example, 'ambition'), the end of the adjective is spelt '-tious' ('ambitious').

2) If the root word ends in 'ce' (for example, 'grace'), the end of the adjective is spelt '-cious' ('gracious').

❶ **Complete** these words with **'-cious'** or **'-tious'**. Use the **root words** in brackets to help you.

a) *My last bedroom was very small but this one is much more spa.. . (space)*

b) *It wasn't a mali.. act. (malice)*

c) *Sweets and cake are very nice, but they're not very nutri.. . (nutrition)*

d) *Is the disease infec..? (infection)*

❷ **Tick** the correct **spelling** in each pair.

a) *superstitious* ☐   *supersticious* ☐

b) *ambitious* ☐   *ambicious* ☐

c) *cautious* ☐   *caucious* ☐

d) *spatious* ☐   *spacious* ☐

Root words: *superstition, ambition, caution, space*

Got it! ☀ ☐   Try again 🔍 ☐   Ask an adult ❓ ☐

WORDS ENDING IN 'CIAL' AND 'TIAL'

Some words end in a 'shul' sound – for example, 'official'. This 'shul' ending may be spelt '-cial' or '-tial':

- 'cial' generally follows a **vowel** (for example, 'special')

- 'tial' generally follows a **consonant** (for example, 'essential')

TIP! There are exceptions to this rule. For example, the 'shul' sound in 'initial' is spelt '-tial' even though it follows a vowel ('i') and in 'financial', '-cial' follows a consonant.

❶ **Complete** the words with **'cial'** or **'tial'**. It may help to identify the vowel or consonant first.

a) *I've never seen such heavy rain. It was absolutely torren..!*

b) *If you ride a bicycle, it is cru.. that the brakes work properly.*

c) *Do you think those flowers are real or artifi..?*

d) *He never really liked so.. occasions, such as parties.*

e) *This will be the President's first offi.. visit.*

❷ **Choose** the correct spelling and put the words in the correct column.

> benefi**cial/tial**   essen**cial/tial**   ra**tial/cial**   substan**tial/cial**
> influen**cial/tial**   spa**tial/cial**

ending in '-cial'	ending in '-tial'

Got it! ☀ ■   Try again 🔍 ■   Ask an adult ❓ ■

WORDS ENDING IN 'ENT' AND 'ANT'

Sometimes the word endings 'ent' and 'ant' can sound the same – for example: *improvement, permanent, president, talent, assistant, brilliant, distant, elephant*

Often, a soft 'g', 'c' or 'qu' is followed by 'ent' – for example, 'agent', 'innocent', 'frequent'.

TIP! If you find the tasks on these spelling endings pages tricky, use the Answers as a handy word list that you can memorise.

---

1 Circle the correct **spelling** in each sentence.

a) *To my [amazemant / amazement], I actually won the competition.*

b) *She's not very [confidant / confident] about speaking up in class.*

c) *The weather was very [pleasant / pleasent].*

d) *Basic language skills are so [important / importent].*

e) *The [pavemants / pavements] here are very narrow.*

2 Complete the words with **'a'** or **'e'**.

a) *Millie had an accid............nt and broke her arm.*

b) *I really wanted to see an eleph............nt.*

c) *My laptop makes a const............nt buzzing sound.*

d) *I found a few fragm............nts of glass on the ground.*

3 Tick the boxes to show whether the **spelling** of the words below is correct or incorrect.

	Correct	Incorrect
a) continant		
b) statement		
c) treatment		
d) elegent		
e) ignorant		

4 **Decide** which word ending is correct, then write the words in the correct column of the table.

> excell**ent/ant**   agreem**ent/ent**   defi**ant/ent**   attend**ant/ent**
> particip**ent/ant**   brilli**ant/ent**   obedi**ent/ant**

ending in '-ent'	ending in '-ant'

5 **Work out** the **mystery words** using these clues.

a) *someone who you are competing against*   o _ _ _ _ _ nt

b) *a piece of paper with important information on it*   d _ _ _ _ _ nt

c) *doing exactly what someone tells you to do*   o _ _ _ _ _ nt

d) *lasting forever*   p _ _ _ _ _ _ nt

e) *something that you say*   co _ _ _ nt

6 **Circle** the **spelling error** in each sentence, then write the correct spelling.

a) *The children had an argument about which instrumant they would play.*

....

b) *She had a presant to give to the president.* ....

c) *There was a minor incidant on the bouncy castle but no other accidents.*

....

d) *Eva was adamant that the statemant was correct.* ....

Got it! ☀ ▢   Try again 🔎 ▢   Ask an adult ❓ ▢

85

WORDS ENDING IN 'ANCE', 'ANCY', 'ENCE' AND 'ENCY'

It can be easy to confuse **nouns** that end in 'ance' and 'ence' (for example, 'guidance' and 'intelligence'). Mistakes can also be made with nouns ending in 'ancy' and 'ency' (for example, 'expectancy' and 'urgency').

If the **adjective** in the same word family ends in 'ant', the noun ends in 'ance' or 'ancy':

> relevant ➜ relevance   tolerant ➜ tolerance   vacant ➜ vacancy

If the adjective in the same word family ends in 'ent', the noun ends in 'ence' or 'ency':

> silent ➜ silence   fluent ➜ fluency   efficient ➜ efficiency
> frequent ➜ frequency

❶ Draw lines to **match** the word beginnings with the word endings.

frequ	ance
vac	ency
excell	ancy
appear	ence

❷ **Complete** the words with the correct ending: **'-ence'**, **'-ance'**, **'-ency'** or **'-ancy'**.

a) He tackled the work with his usual effici....................... .

b) The audi....................... clapped loudly when she came on stage.

c) It was a brilliant perform....................... by this young actor.

d) It's such a nuis....................... having to go all the way home and collect your kit!

❸ **Tick** the boxes to show whether the words below are spelt correctly or incorrectly.

		Correct	Incorrect
a)	emergancy	☐	☐
b)	evidence	☐	☐
c)	referance	☐	☐
d)	currency	☐	☐

4 **Complete** the crossword using the words from the box and the clues below.

sentence expectancy balance silence fluency distance

Across
4 how much space there is between two places
5 your ability to stay upright and not fall
6 Your life .... is how long you are expected to live
Down
1 when there is no noise
2 a group of words starting with a capital letter and ending with a full stop
3 how good someone is at speaking a language

5 **Circle** the **spelling error** in each sentence, then write the correct spelling in the space provided.

a) *Violance in films can be upsetting.* ....

b) *He was an actor before his presidancy.* ....

c) *Dog training teaches the importence of obedience.* ....

d) *That has no relevence to the discussion!* ....

Got it! ☀ ❑   Try again 🔍 ❑   Ask an adult ❓ ❑

87

WORDS ENDING IN 'ABLE', 'IBLE', 'ABLY' AND 'IBLY'

Some **adjectives** end in '-able' or '-ible' – for example, 'enjoyable' and 'incredible'.

In the same way, some **adverbs** end in '-ably' or '-ibly' – for example, 'considerably' and 'terribly'.

If the adjective in the same word family ends in 'able', the adverb ends in 'ably':

  miserable ➔ *miserably* *probable* ➔ *probably* *reasonable* ➔ *reasonably*

If the adjective in the same word family ends in 'ible', the adverb ends in 'ibly':

  terrible ➔ *terribly* *impossible* ➔ *impossibly* *horrible* ➔ *horribly*

Sometimes, when a root word ends in a soft 'c' sound spelled '-ce' or a soft 'g' sound spelled '-ge', you need to keep the 'e' before adding the suffix '-able':

  change ➔ *changeable* *replace* ➔ *replaceable* *notice* ➔ *noticeable*

1 **Circle** the correct **endings**.

a) *I'll prob**ably / ibly** see you at Isabel's house.*

b) *She very sens**ably / ibly** decided to save her money.*

c) *It's going to be cold so make sure you dress suit**ibly / ably**.*

d) *Lara was vis**ibly / ably** upset by his comments.*

2 **Tick** the correct **spelling** in each pair.

a) *capable* ☐ *capible* ☐

b) *horribly* ☐ *horrably* ☐

c) *memorible* ☐ *memorable* ☐

d) *visible* ☐ *visable* ☐

3 Draw lines to **match** the sentence halves.

She's a very lik	*ably the best café in town.*
This is argu	*ibly sad.*
The writing is very clear and access	*able character.*
I found the whole film terr	*ible for children.*

4 **Complete** the words with the endings **'-ible'** or **'-able'**.

a) There are three syll.....................s in the word 'terrible'.

b) I find chocolate irresist...................... .

c) I can't write a whole essay in half an hour – that's imposs......................!

d) Puppies are just so lov...................... .

e) You have to be really flex...................... to be a gymnast.

5 **Circle** the **spelling error** in each sentence, then write the correct spelling.

a) It's incredable that something so small can be so valuable. ....

b) Dan's cooking is terrible. Everything he makes is inedable. ....

c) The heat was unbearible. I found it impossible to go out in the day. ....

6 **Write** sentences that contain these words.

a) reliable

....

....

b) possibly

....

....

c) unbearably

....

....

Got it! ☼ ▢   Try again 🔍 ▢   Ask an adult ❓ ▢

'i' before 'e' except after 'c''

This well-known saying helps you remember that in most words, **'i' comes before 'e'** – for example, 'achieve', 'brief'.

However, if the letter that comes before these vowels is 'c', you **change the order to 'ei'** – for example, 'deceive'.

...but only when it rhymes with 'tree'

This second part of the saying reminds you that the rule ('i' before 'e' except after 'c') is only true when the sound made by 'ie' or 'ei' **rhymes with 'tree'**. For example, 'ancient' doesn't rhyme with 'tree', so 'ie' comes after 'c'.

Other rule-breakers are:

- Words like 'their' and 'weight', which have 'ei' but do not rhyme with tree or follow 'c'

- Words like 'weird', 'protein' and 'seize', which have 'ei' even though they rhyme with 'tree' and do not follow 'c'

❶ **Complete** these words by filling in the **missing letters**.

a) *rec _ _ pt*

b) *c _ _ ling*

c) *th _ _ f*

d) *f _ _ ld*

❷ **Tick** the correct **spelling** in each pair.

a) *peice* ☐   *piece*

b) *receive*   *recieve* ☐

c) *brief*   *breif* ☐

d) *releif*   *relief*

❸ Circle the **spelling error** in each sentence, then write the correct spelling.

a) It was my neice's eighth birthday yesterday. ....

b) My neighbour recieved a big bunch of flowers through the post today.

   ....

c) My best freind likes really weird food combinations. ....

d) The receipt was written on a scrappy peice of paper. ....

❹ Circle the correct **spelling**.

a) The dog he was holding looked really [fierce / feirce].

b) Her top was pink and her trousers were [biege / beige] .

c) Their standards of [hygiene / hygeine] are fairly poor.

d) Are you eating enough [protein / protien] ?

e) Do you know where [thier / their] house is?

❺ Tick the boxes to show if the words below are spelt correctly or incorrectly.

	Correct	Incorrect
a) weird		
b) acheive		
c) weigh		
d) seize		
e) decieve		

'OUGH' WORDS

The letter combination 'ough' is found in a lot of English words, so it is worth remembering. The interesting thing about this letter combination is that it is pronounced in many different ways. Consider the following:

In 'dough', it sounds like 'oh'.

In 'through', it sounds like 'oo'.

In 'thorough', it sounds like 'uh'.

In 'tough' it sounds like 'uff'.

In 'cough', it sounds like 'off'.

In 'bought', it sounds like 'or'.

In 'drought', it sounds like 'ow'.

1 Write down the sounds that **'ough'** makes in each of these words: 'uff' or 'oa'/'ow'.

a) *rough* ....

b) *dough* ....

c) *though* ....

d) *enough* ....

e) *tough* ....

f) *although* ....

2 **Write** the words from the box in the correct column of the table, according to the sound that **'ough'** makes in the word.

> doughnut   thorough   enough   brought   nought   tough
> though   sought

oh	uh	or	uff

3 **Unscramble** the letters in brackets to make a word to complete the sentences.

a) *Eva has a sore throat and a bad [ohcgu]* ....

b) *You really [hogut]* .... *to work a bit harder.*

c) *Have you had [gouneh]* .... *to eat, Tom?*

d) *I [gobuht]* .... *some bread and milk from the supermarket.*

 Got it! ☀ ▢   Try again ◯ ▢   Ask an adult ? ▢

SILENT LETTERS AND UNSTRESSED VOWELS

Sometimes a letter makes no sound when you say a word. It is easy to forget these letters when you are writing that word. For example, the letters 'g' and 'k' are **silent** before the letter 'n' in the words 'de**s**ign', 'gnash' and 'knee'.

Other letters that can be silent are 'h', 'b', 'w' and 't' – for example, 'ghost', 'bomb', 'sword', 'castle'.

Some words contain **vowels** that are said very clearly. For example, the 'a' sounds like the 'a' in 'mat'. Other words have vowels that are not said clearly.

A word may contain an unstressed 'a', 'e', 'i' or 'o' that sounds like 'u'. For example, the word 'zebra' sounds as if it is spelt 'zebruh'. Other words have vowels that you can't hear. For example, the word 'different' sounds as if it is spelt 'diffrent'.

1 **Circle** the **silent letters** in the words below.

a) wreck f) design

b) knuckle g) know

c) doubt h) limb

d) foreign i) gnaw

e) fasten j) wheel

2 **Underline** the word in each sentence that is missing a **silent letter**.

a) Queen Victoria reined for sixty-three years.

b) Be careful with that sharp nife!

c) Your bike has bigger weels.

d) We climed a mountain while we were on holiday.

e) She whisled to her dog.

❸ **Circle** the words that have an **unstressed 'e'**.

present   separate   accident   general   offer   medicine

❹ **Circle** the words that have an **unstressed 'a'**.

factory   petal   hospital   similar   library   fabulous

❺ **Complete** the words below with their **unstressed vowels**.

a) defin _ te

f) calend _ r

b) fact _ ry

g) sep _ rate

c) med _ cine

h) bus _ ness

d) angr _ ly

i) veg _ table

e) freed _ m

j) choc _ late

❻ **Circle** the word with the missing **unstressed vowel**, then write the word correctly.

a) It was a very exciting film but quite frighting in parts. ....

b) The two exercises are quite diffrent. ....

c) It's a very useful refrence book. ....

d) The first chapter gives you a lot of genral information. ....

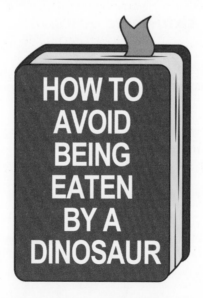

HOW TO
AVOID
BEING
EATEN
BY A
DINOSAUR

Got it! ☀ ▢   Try again 🔍 ▢   Ask an adult ❓ ▢

HOMOPHONES

Homophones are words that sound the same but are spelt differently and mean something completely different.

Examples of homophones are the words 'hear' and 'here'. These words sound the same but 'hear' means 'to have a sound come through your ears' and 'here' means 'to this place':

Did you hear that noise?

Come here and look at this!

1 **Circle** the correct **homophone** from each pair.

a) *If you leave your bike there, someone might [steel / steal] it.*

b) *This is our house and that's [their / there] house.*

c) *I can't decide which dress to [wear / where] to the party.*

d) *We picked some delicious [pairs / pears] from the tree.*

e) *Where do I [right / write] my name?*

2 **Complete** the sentences using the correct word from the **homophone** pairs in the box.

> weight / wait   too / to   except / accept   weak / week   tale / tail

a) *The dog wagged her .... happily.*

b) *I couldn't .... to meet my new baby sister!*

c) *I'll see you next ....*

d) *I couldn't .... money from her.*

e) *I didn't go to the party. I was just .... tired.*

Got it! ☀ ▢   Try again 🔎 ▢   Ask an adult ❓ ▢

❸ Complete the sentences using all the **homophones** in the box.

> dear / deer   die / dye   root / route

a) I think I might .... my hair a different colour.

b) You need to get hold of the plant by its .... to pull it up.

c) We briefly saw a .... in the forest before it ran off.

d) If they can't find any food, these animals will ....

e) .... Anna, I'm writing to invite you to our party!

f) I'm going to take a different .... to college today.

❹ Circle the incorrect **homophone** in each sentence, then write down the correct one.

a) I'm sure Grandad will be delighted if you right him a letter. ....

b) The mail bird is smaller and has a very beautiful tail. ....

c) I've bean to so many good cafés in this city. ....

d) It's a terrible waist of food to throw it away like that. ....

e) I wonder weather Sophie has some clothes that we can borrow. ....

❺ Write a **homophone** for each of the words below.

a) bare ....

b) flower ....

c) night ....

d) pair ....

e) steal ....

Answer these SATS-style questions on spelling and vocabulary and then complete the spelling test.

❶ Which sentence uses the hyphen correctly?

Tick **one**.

You can pre-order the game online. ☑

My dad said he thought it was il-legal. ☐

Could you un-plug the laptop, please? ☐

❷ Circle the suffixes in the sentence below.

This flower is very special as it symbolises happiness and health.

❸ Draw a line to match each prefix with its meaning.

mis- (e.g. 'misspell')	not or opposite
re- (e.g. 'rejoin')	wrong
dis- (e.g. 'disagree')	too much
over- (e.g. 'overeat')	again

SPELLING TASK

You will need to use the online audio file **www.yorknotes.com/primary/ks2/english/tests** to help you with this SATs-style task.

Listen to each sentence and write down the correct spelling of the missing word.

❶ My sister has various food ....

❷ Ava looked .... at the plate of food.

❸ The palace is the .... home of the president.

❹ My .... and nephew came to stay.

❺ .... trainers are these?

❻ .... are often seen in urban areas.

❼ At my uncle's wedding, there was a .... to entertain the guests.

❽ .... not going to the party, are you?

❾ I don't have .... money to buy a scooter.

❿ Would you like a .... of cake?

Well done, you've completed this Targeted Skills and Test Practice book! Give yourself a pat on the back!

PART ONE: GRAMMAR BASICS

NOUNS

1 a) laptop, apple

  b) Paris, Daniel

  c) pen, cat

  d) flock, bunch

  e) happiness, truth

2 a) Johnny has <u>a smart, black scooter</u>.

  b) Mrs Taylor is <u>a really good teacher</u>.

  c) <u>A pack of wolves</u> roams the forest.

  d) We have <u>an extremely grumpy old dog</u>.

  e) <u>A very excited little boy</u> ran up to me.

ADJECTIVES

1 a) I had a <u>delicious</u> bowl of pasta.

  b) Finn found the experience <u>terrifying</u>.

  c) Your bag is so much <u>smaller</u> than mine.

2   babyish

    likeable

    helpful

3   Of all the animals that we saw, the lions were may favourite. They looked so <u>strong</u> with their muscular back legs, and yet so grace<u>ful</u> at the same time. And their faces were really <u>striking</u> – I've never seen more beautiful animals. The guinea pigs were also sweet and <u>cuddly</u>. I couldn't imagine how guinea pigs could survive in the wild. They looked so hel<u>pless</u> with their short little legs.

PRONOUNS

1 and 2 We left a message for Sophie but <u>she</u> hasn't replied.

    George and Ethan go to tennis club and <u>they</u> really enjoy it.

    My brother used to have guitar lessons but <u>he</u>'s given it up.

    Klara and I saw <u>him</u> in concert and <u>we</u> loved him.

3 a) … she was too busy

  b) … they couldn't stay.

  c) … they loved them.

  d) … he ignored her.

4

Personal pronouns	Possessive pronouns
he	theirs
they	hers
we	ours
you	mine
	his

5 a) Personal pronoun

  b) Personal pronoun

  c) Possessive pronoun

  d) Personal pronoun

  e) Possessive pronoun

  f) Possessive pronoun

6   *Possible answers:*

  b) … she stayed at home.

  c) … we left without them.

  d) … we had burgers instead.

  e) … gave me his.

RELATIVE PRONOUNS

1 a) We visited the park (where) we used to play together.

  b) Are those the girls (who) went to your school?

  c) That's the woman (whose) daughter won the dance competition.

  d) This is the game (that) Charlotte bought for me.

2 a) I told Alice I'd called her, which was the truth. ✓

DETERMINERS

1 a) My grandmother had <u>five</u> sisters and <u>two</u> brothers.

  b) <u>Those</u> T-shirts are really cool but <u>these</u> ones are cheaper.

  c) <u>My</u> aunt bought me <u>a</u> sweater with a picture of <u>an</u> apple on it.

  d) <u>His</u> mum gave us <u>a</u> picnic and <u>some</u> money.

  e) <u>The</u> people who lost <u>their</u> dog found him down <u>a</u> hole in <u>a</u> field.

2 a) Olivia's uncle is <u>an</u> author.

  b) He's written <u>a</u> book on the Arctic.

  c) It's <u>the</u> longest book I've ever seen.

VERBS

1 a) Thieves <u>stole</u> the necklace.

  b) We <u>hammered</u> on the door.

  c) It <u>poured</u> with rain for two whole days.

  d) I really <u>love</u> my new art class

2 a) Past

  b) Future

  c) Present

  d) Past

3 a) We usually (take) the path by the stream.

  b) Alfie and Leo (were) at the cinema too.

  c) Ella's teacher (is) going to give her some extra help.

  d) My little sister (eats) way more than me!

4 a) I've already <u>done</u> my homework.

  b) We <u>took</u> the ball to the park and played football.

  c) Last summer we <u>went</u> to Spain for our holidays.

  d) When I was seven, I <u>had</u> a skating party.

5 b) I <u>am</u> crazy about football.

  c) She <u>has</u> swimming lessons on Saturday.

  d) He <u>likes</u> to make his own sushi.

ADVERBS

1 a) I <u>accidentally</u> knocked the glass over.

  b) <u>Perhaps</u> Lily would like to come.

  c) She <u>quickly</u> lost interest in the subject.

  d) He's <u>very</u> excited today.

  e) She <u>reluctantly</u> agreed to come.

  f) I'll <u>certainly</u> help you if I can.

  g) I <u>definitely</u> put the book back after I'd finished with it.

2 a) Verb

  b) Adjective

  c) Adjective

  d) Verb

  e) Verb

3 a) She's very old now, so she walks very <u>slowly</u>.

  b) It's cold and wet out there, so make sure you dress <u>suitably</u>.

  c) <u>Suddenly</u>, without any warning, she shouted out, 'No!'

  d) He's <u>quite</u> tall, but not huge.

e) I've never seen anyone so thin. He's <u>incredibly</u> slim!

4 *Possible answers:*

b) travel a lot

c) go to the cinema

d) join the tennis club

e) see Harry

5 *Possible answers:*

a) fast

b) carefully

c) easily

d) really

e) so

6 *Pupils' own answers*

ADVERBIALS

1 a) Leo and I see each other <u>once a week</u>.

b) Mum and Amelia spoke <u>in hushed voices</u>.

c) Max had forgotten to wear a watch. <u>Consequently</u>, he was late.

d) I'm meeting Harry <u>in five minutes</u>.

2 Hurry, Alfie! The film starts in two minutes!

Mala ate until her plate was empty.

She closed her eyes and slept peacefully.

I still see him from time to time.

3 a) As fast as my legs could carry me, I ran from the house.

b) All night long, the wind whistled and the wolves howled.

c) Under the boughs of the old yew tree, we sheltered from the rain.

d) Without a moment's hesitation, she replied.

e) Before I start, could you all switch off your mobile phones?

4 *Possible answers:*

a) slowly and wearily.

b) twice a week.

c) for what seemed like ages.

d) However

e) In the end

PREPOSITIONS

1 a) We're heading <u>towards</u> London.

b) I put my trainers on <u>before</u> going for a run.

c) The school was closed <u>because of</u> staff shortages.

d) We got there <u>after</u> you.

e) We didn't eat <u>until</u> nine o'clock.

2 a) I set the plates down <u>on</u> the table.

b) It was raining so we sheltered <u>under</u> a tree.

c) She broke her ankle after she fell <u>down</u> a flight of stairs.

d) Why don't you stay <u>with</u> me and keep me company?

3 We both crawled <u>into</u> the cave, first me, then Jess. <u>Inside</u> the cave it was dark and damp. Water splashed <u>on</u> our heads. I could hear Jess breathing heavily <u>behind</u> me. I found my torch and pressed <u>down</u> the switch, but it wouldn't work. Perhaps the batteries were flat. Slowly my eyes started to adjust, and I began to make out vague shapes, just <u>beyond</u> my reach. Suddenly a strange rumbling sound came from <u>below</u> us, and we both jumped!

4 *Possible answers:*

a) When I saw Isabel, she was walking <u>towards the library.</u>

b) I put my bag <u>in the drawer.</u>

5 *Pupils' own answers*

SATs PRACTICE

1 I didn't want to spoil my <u>friendship</u> with Amy.

Sadly, the singer's <u>childhood</u> was not especially happy.

People often feel great <u>love</u> for their pets.

2 It's the most beautiful sunset I've ever seen. ✓

3 We saw <u>an</u> elephant.

It was <u>a</u> wild elephant.

It was <u>the</u> most enormous animal I've ever seen.

4 In the morning, we'll go swimming.

5 Jack and Archie called round and <u>they</u> brought <u>me</u> a present for <u>my</u> birthday.

6

Sentence	Verb	Adjective	Adverb
It was <u>so</u> hot in the classroom today!		✓	
Millie spoke <u>clearly</u>.	✓		
She won <u>very</u> easily.			✓

7 Dad was really <u>furious</u>. ➔ adjective

The racket is <u>mine</u>. ➔ pronoun

I'll <u>possibly</u> see you on Saturday. ➔ adverb

<u>Those</u> milkshakes look so good! ➔ determiner

PART TWO: SENTENCE GRAMMAR

TYPES OF SENTENCES

1 a) What an enormous house you have!

b) How do you open this window?

c) Elephants come from Africa and Asia.

d) Run for your lives!

e) Jason is very sporty, isn't he?

PHRASES AND CLAUSES

1 b) juicy cucumber ✓

c) a scary giant centipede ✓

d) going to the shops ✓

2 a) <u>Jo overslept on Monday</u> because she had been to a party.

b) Although it was raining, <u>Saj didn't wear a coat</u>.

c) Even if it is a silly game, <u>Marge will play</u>.

d) <u>The plants won't grow</u> unless it rains.

e) When he saw the homework, <u>Ronnie sighed to himself</u>.

3 and 4

<u>Even when the match is rubbish</u>, I love going to see City play.

She washed her hands thoroughly <u>before preparing the salad</u>.

<u>Although I love sci-fi</u>, detective films are great too.

Our dog is slow and grumpy <u>even though he is still young</u>.

<u>Unless you know the answer</u>, don't put your hand up.

5 *Possible answer:*

Kate brushed her hair before she went to the party.

6 *Possible answers:*

b) Umar explained to Daisy that he was too busy to help her.

c) Ice-creams make a mess even if you are careful.

d) You will never beat me unless you cheat.

RELATIVE CLAUSES

1 a) We went to a theme park, <u>which was fantastic</u>!

b) The man, <u>whose name was Daniel Khan</u>, was a dentist.

c) Where is the pen <u>that I lent you</u>?

d) The house in London, <u>where I lived with my parents</u>, was tiny.

e) I gave my old bike to Lexie, <u>who was very pleased with it</u>.

2 a) The pizza <u>that</u> I chose was a vegetarian one.

b) We went to the Van Gogh museum, <u>which</u> is in Amsterdam.

c) That's the woman <u>who</u> shouted at me.

d) Do you remember the time <u>when</u> we got lost?

e) That's the place <u>where</u> my granddad was born.

3 a) Is she the woman (who) stole your money?

b) We're having my favourite meal, (which) is chicken.

c) The holiday (that) I enjoyed most was in Spain.

4 She showed me the cupboard where they keep the pens and paper.

She's the lady whose car broke down.

That was the time when Dad lost his passport.

This is the key which unlocks the back door.

5 a) This is the ring that I found. ✓

b) Have you seen the painting which Lottie did? ✓

6 a) Do you remember the day when Sofia dropped her phone in the river?

b) I'd like to see that letter that (or which) Grandpa wrote when he was in the army.

c) She gave me some medicine that (or which) made my cough much better.

FORMING SENTENCES

1 a) compound

b) simple

c) complex

d) compound

2 Ella can't play football because she's broken her leg.

Although he doesn't speak French, he had a wonderful time in Paris.

Unless we get a bigger car, we won't be able to take everyone.

Dad says he'll take me out for a pizza if I get a good school report.

We had a great time at the seaside even though it rained all day.

3 a) If you don't understand the question, ask your teacher. ✓

c) Unless we leave now, we won't get there in time. ✓

4 a) Even though Dad was tired, he (still) played football with us.

b) While I was eating my tea, the phone rang.

c) Our visitors were late because they got lost.

5 *Possible answers:*

a) Freya is really good on the drums but I can't play them at all.

b) My school is very big.

c) If you want to make friends, you should join a club.

CO-ORDINATING CONJUNCTIONS

1 a) It was a hot summer's day <u>and</u> the sun was shining.

b) It was getting dark, <u>so</u> we decided to go inside.

c) You can come with us now <u>or</u> you can meet us later.

2 a) I wanted to buy the game, <u>but</u> it was too expensive.

b) The door opened <u>and</u> the president walked in.

c) My rabbit was ill <u>so</u> I took him to the vet.

d) It's possible to go by bus <u>or</u> to take a train.

3 a) Shall we watch TV <u>or</u> shall we listen to music?

b) I sing in a choir <u>and</u> I play drums in a band.

c) I saw a thief <u>so</u> I called the police.

SUBORDINATING CONJUNCTIONS

1 a) We'll be late (unless) we hurry up.

b) (Because) Maddy was ill, she didn't go to school.

c) (While) we were walking to school, we saw a car accident.

d) I won't buy the tickets (if) they're very expensive.

2 I learned to speak German when we lived in Berlin.

Eva ate her spinach even though she didn't like it much.

You can put your coat on if you feel chilly.

We were late because our car broke down.

CONNECTING SENTENCES AND PARAGRAPHS

1 a) Consequently

b) However

c) Firstly

d) Later on

2 a) 4

b) 1

c) 5

d) 2

e) 3

STANDARD AND NON-STANDARD ENGLISH

1 a) I think she (does) understand you.

b) We saw a fox when we (were) in the wood.

c) Ruby and Poppy (go) to school with me.

d) I don't think our teacher (was) very pleased.

2 b) Those cakes are delicious. ✔

c) I've got some new shoes. I really like them. ✔

3 a) I haven't got (any) money.

b) There (was) no food left.

c) She didn't give us (any) advice.

d) There (were) no people in the building.

4 a) Incorrect

b) Correct

c) Incorrect

d) Incorrect

e) Correct

5 a) He can't have eaten all those cakes. ✓

   d) She hasn't got any friends. ✓

SATs PRACTICE

1 We won't need the umbrella ➜ unless it rains.

   If you need an umbrella, ➜ you can borrow this one.

   You should take an umbrella ➜ because it's raining.

2 It's cold in here, isn't it? ✓

3 I listened to the album, but I didn't like it. ✓

4

Sentence	Main clause	Subordinate clause
We left home <u>as soon as everyone was ready</u>.		✓
Although she's young, <u>she's not very fit</u>.	✓	
<u>Because Emma's quite shy</u>, she didn't want to come to the party.		✓

5 It was a hot day <u>so</u> we didn't need our coats.

   I ate the soup <u>although</u> I didn't like it very much.

   Shall we play chess <u>or</u> shall we go swimming?

6 whose ✓

7 How cold it is tonight! ➜ exclamation

   Open your books on page 17. ➜ command

   Our house has three bedrooms. ➜ statement

   Where is the railway station? ➜ question

8

Sentence	Standard English	Non-standard English
Could we use some of those pencils, please?	✓	
I haven't got no brothers or sisters.		✓
I met Mia when we was both in Year 2.		✓
You should have asked the teacher for help.	✓	

9 (While) our parents were busy, my brother and I did some painting and watched TV.

10 I think you could have tried harder.

PART THREE: VERB FORMS AND TENSES

SIMPLE PAST AND SIMPLE PRESENT

1 a) Past

   b) Past

   c) Present

   d) Past

   e) Present

2 a) My parents (paid) me for washing the car.

   b) We (hid) behind a tree.

   c) Hannah (swam) fifty lengths.

   d) We (stayed) in a nice hotel.

3 b) She said she was sorry. ✓

   c) We found some money in the street. ✓

4 a) hoped

   b) threw

   c) worked

   d) drove

   e) flew

   f) wrote

5 a) Alex <u>went</u> to school by bus.

   b) We <u>grew</u> lots of vegetables.

c) I <u>told</u> her all my news.

d) I <u>knew</u> Peter.

6   *Possible answers:*

The man plays golf / hits the golf ball.

The man played golf / hit the golf ball.

VERBS IN THE PERFECT FORM

1 a) I twisted my ankle and it has <u>swollen</u> up.

b) The show had <u>finished</u> by the time we arrived.

c) Had your brother <u>been</u> to Germany before?

d) My sister has a new boyfriend, but I haven't <u>met</u> him yet.

2 a) Amber <u>hasn't</u> done her homework yet.

b) My friends <u>have</u> made me a birthday cake.

c) I <u>haven't</u> been to New York, but I really want to!

d) <u>Have</u> you visited your aunty recently?

3 a) Mum's <u>thrown</u> away my old coat because it was ripped.

b) Anna hasn't <u>played</u> tennis for a long time.

c) I've <u>put</u> the apples in a bowl.

4 a) stolen

b) run

c) slept

d) bitten

5 b) <u>Have</u> you <u>fed</u> the cat today?

c) Oh no! Someone <u>has drunk</u> all the milk.

d) I was sure that I <u>had met</u> the woman before.

PRESENT AND PAST PROGRESSIVE

1 a) We (were) going to London.

b) Lois and Petra (are) having their dinner.

c) (Were) you expecting to see Damia?

d) I (am) reading a really good book.

2 b) Dan learned French while he <u>was working</u> in Paris.

c) Jade couldn't hear me because she <u>was listening</u> to some loud music.

d) I'll call the children. They <u>are playing</u> outside at the moment.

MODAL VERBS

1 b) Sasha might be moving to Mexico. ✓

c) Rick won't play tennis with me. ✓

2 a) I'm not sure if Emma (can) hear us.

b) It looks as if it (might) rain later.

c) If you have to get up early, you (shouldn't) be late to bed.

d) I don't think I (would) ever try bungee jumping.

3 a) I was annoyed because Millie (wouldn't) lend me a pen.

b) Ben ran off before I (could) tell him.

c) Please give this letter to your Mum or Dad. It's very important, so you (mustn't) lose it.

4 a) We <u>might</u> go away for Christmas but we're not sure yet.

b) If someone is bullying you at school, you <u>should</u> tell a teacher.

c) The coach leaves at nine o'clock and it won't wait for anyone, so you really <u>mustn't</u> be late!

d) Unfortunately, I <u>couldn't</u> go to the party because I was ill.

5 b) Tennis wouldn't be a good sport for you.

   c) Pablo will help us.

   d) You mustn't eat all the food.

SATs PRACTICE

1   I didn't know you had lost my number. ✓

2   I <u>can't</u> play the guitar.

    Everyone in the school <u>must</u> wear the school uniform.

    You <u>shouldn't</u> go swimming straight after a meal.

3   I ⟨met⟩ Mason at the sports centre and we ⟨went⟩ swimming together.

4   has fixed ✓

5

	Past simple	Past progressive
The children were getting on the coach.		✓
We all sat on the floor.	✓	
Brandon was eating his dinner.		✓

6   I will win the competition. ✓

7   We need to be quiet. Dad <u>is working</u> in the next room.

    My sisters <u>are making</u> some cakes for tea.

PART FOUR: PUNCTUATION

CAPITALS AND FULL STOPS

1   Paris ✓

    Tuesday ✓

    David ✓

    October ✓

2 a) Incorrect

   b) Correct

   c) Incorrect

QUESTION MARKS AND EXCLAMATION MARKS

1 b) Why do I need to bring a coat?

   c) Who gave you those sweets?

   d) You must leave the building immediately!

2 a) .

   b) !

   c) ?

   d) ?

COMMAS 1

1 a) 4

   b) 5

   c) 4

   d) 4

2 a) I gave cards to Mum, Dad, Kyle and Ben.

   b) We spent the whole day polishing, scrubbing, dusting, hoovering and cooking.

   c) My next door neighbour is unfriendly, rude, noisy and bossy.

   d) My favourite subjects are History, Religious Studies, French and English.

3 a) Incorrect

   b) Correct

   c) Incorrect

   d) Correct

4 a) I'm going to make a pasta sauce. I need to buy <u>tomatoes, onions, oil and herbs</u>.

   b) For our camping trip, I need to take <u>a torch, a sleeping bag and a water bottle</u>.

5 *Possible answers:*

a) Jack's best friend is kind, funny and generous.

b) In my grandparents' living room, they have a sofa, an armchair, a rug, a lamp and a TV.

c) Arlo's really sporty. He's good at running, swimming, karate and gymnastics.

COMMAS 2

1 a) Correct

b) Correct

c) Incorrect

d) Incorrect

2 a) I felt cold, so I shut the window.

b) My brother fell over and he broke his leg.

c) I wanted a sandwich, but we didn't have any bread.

d) I didn't eat the pizza because I don't like cheese.

COMMAS 3

1 a) After school, I hope to go to university.

b) We were all tired. Nevertheless, we decided to continue our climb.

c) We weren't sure what to do. In the end, we decided to go home.

d) The hotel provides all meals. In addition, free drinks are available all day.

2 a) Because the roads were icy, Mum had to drive slowly.

b) If you are cold, you can put the heating on.

c) Unless you feel better later, you won't be able to go to the show.

d) Although Amber can't swim, she still enjoys playing in the water.

3 b) Unless you call her, your mum will be worried. *or* Unless you call your mum, she will be worried.

c) When the teacher wasn't looking, we drew silly pictures.

d) If you want to, you can come with me.

4 a) Correct

b) Incorrect

c) Incorrect

d) Correct

COMMAS 4

1 a) The train, despite stopping several times, arrived on time.

b) The city, which attracts a lot of tourists, is quite large.

c) The children, even the older ones, all enjoyed the circus.

d) My neighbour, Mrs Ashton, is a nurse at the local hospital.

2 a) Correct

b) Incorrect

c) Correct

d) Incorrect

3 a) The cat, whose name was Ginger, let us stroke him.

b) We went to Miller's, a music shop, to buy a recorder.

c) Her hair, which is very long, is brown.

d) The meeting, which is only two days away, will be very important.

4 a) I had to go and see the headteacher, Mrs White, in her office.

b) You should ask my friend, Katya Smith, to help you.

5 a) They visited Brunei, a small country in Asia, last month.

b) Bill Fowler, my dad's boss, invited us to a barbecue.

c) The club, which has over 100 members, meets every Saturday.

BRACKETS AND DASHES

1 a) We had to take Fatma (my cousin) to the station.

b) We managed to find the cinema (in the end).

c) We're having chicken curry (which I love) for dinner.

d) Everyone was happy except Annie (who had a bad headache).

2 a) Make sure you do your homework – all of it – before you go to bed.

b) Mr Ross – one of the teachers at my school – gave me this book.

c) He brought his luggage – all twelve suitcases of it – with him.

d) Go and pick some tomatoes – big ones if you can – for lunch.

3 a) My parents are – I hope – getting me a bike for my birthday.

b) Dexter (Lee's brother) painted this picture.

c) Tickets (which are only £5) are available from the school office.

d) I enjoy playing cricket – and other sports – at school.

4 a) My uncle – the one with the sports car – is coming to visit next week.

b) Five hundred people – many of them children – were at the event.

c) My mum lived in Stapleford – a village near Cambridge – for five years.

5 a) I gave my best friend (Cara Phipps) a bracelet.

b) I really enjoyed his latest movie (especially the special effects).

c) I wore my dress (the blue one).

d) That boy (the one with black hair) is my cousin.

SPEECH PUNCTUATION

1 a) Correct

b) Incorrect

c) Incorrect

d) Correct

2 a) No

b) Yes

c) No

d) No

3 a) 'I recognise you⟨,⟩said the man. 'We met at Marc's party.' 2

b) Gavin asked, ⟨'⟩are you hungry?' 3

c) 'I hope⟨,⟩said Izzie, 'that you will be happy here.' 1

d) 'It's late,' said Dad. ⟨'⟩You should go to bed.' 3

4 a) 'You never know,' said Fiona, 'what might happen next.' ✓

b) The police officer said, 'Stand back, please!' ✓

c) 'Hey, Beth!' said Zoe, 'How are you?' ✓

d) 'Can you help me, please?' begged Arianna. ✓

5 a) 'This is Mark,' said Summer. 'He's my brother.'

b) 'I think,' whispered Lou, 'that she likes us.'

c) 'Hey!' shouted Katie. 'What are you doing?'

d) 'It's not a mouse,' said Georgie. 'It's a rat.'

6 a) 'Is dinner ready?' asked Jan.

   b) The man yelled, 'Look out!'

   c) 'I don't think,' said Adam, 'that you should go there.'

7 'I'm scared,' whispered Callum. 'It's too dark in here.' / 'Don't be such a baby,' his sister replied. / 'We'll be in trouble if Mum finds out,' Callum continued. / 'She isn't going to find out,' his sister muttered, 'unless you tell her.'

8 b) Rosie said (that) the money was in the bank.

   c) Sami said (that) he'd lost his coat.

APOSTROPHES 1

1 a) I would

   b) We will

   c) You have

   d) I am

2 a) <u>Where's</u> my pen

   b) Do you think <u>you'll</u> pass the test?

   c) Ryan <u>can't</u> ride a bike yet.

   d) I think <u>I've</u> broken my leg.

3 a) hadn't

   b) she'd

   c) won't

   d) shouldn't

   e) he's

   f) can't

4 a) Peter <u>wouldn't</u> lend me his pencil.

   b) I thought <u>she'd</u> read the book before.

   c) My friends are still up in the mountains. I hope <u>they'll</u> be OK.

   d) I think <u>you're</u> right about this movie.

5 a) Incorrect

   b) Correct

   c) Incorrect

   d) Correct

6 a) I found this ring – I think <u>it's</u> Marta's.

   b) This jigsaw should be easy – <u>its</u> pieces are quite big.

   c) We can't call Kerry – <u>it's</u> the middle of the night.

   d) I don't like this shirt because <u>its</u> sleeves are too long.

APOSTROPHES 2

1 a) My friends stroked the <u>cats</u> soft fur.

   b) <u>Megans</u> mum likes baking cookies.

   c) We helped to carry Mrs <u>Millers</u> bags.

2 a) Incorrect

   b) Correct

   c) Correct

3 b) my parents' car

   c) the saucepan's handle

   d) the sun's heat

4 a) I am going to borrow my <u>friend's</u> bike.

   b) We spoke to the <u>elephants'</u> owners.

   c) He told us the <u>elephant's</u> name.

   d) My dad can never remember my <u>friends'</u> names.

5 a) Farouk's

   b) team's

   c) Tom's

   d) children's

6 a) My <u>sister's</u> jumper is full of holes.

   b) We had tomatoes and <u>Mum's</u> home-made bread.

   c) Someone had let down my <u>bike's</u> tyres.

   d) The <u>castle's</u> walls were very thick.

SATs PRACTICE

1 Have you seen <u>Rileys</u> photos? He went to Mallorca, to stay in his <u>familys</u> apartment there. The beaches look awesome!

2 'What time is it?' asked Yusuf. ✓

3 There should be a comma after 'shy'. ✓

   There should be a comma between 'kind' and 'funny'. ✓

4 Mrs Botha (my next-door neighbour) is a train driver.

5 Our van is very old, so it doesn't go very fast. ✓

6 What an unusual building ✓

7 <u>You will</u> meet Joe on Sunday. <u>He is</u> great fun. <u>I have</u> known him for a long time.

8 I got a jigsaw puzzle, a kite, a football and some sweets for my birthday.

9 Is Anna a dancer?

10 My friends, apart from Shahena, all live in the city. ✓

11 'This is fantastic,' Bao said. ✓

PART FIVE: SPELLING AND VOCABULARY

WORD FAMILIES

1 b) photo
  c) vac
  d) bio
  e) port

2 a) photo
  b) port
  c) bio
  d) phon
  e) vac

PLURALS

1 a) roofs ✓
  b) knives ✓
  c) foxes ✓
  d) sheep ✓
  e) potatoes ✓

2 a) tomato<u>es</u>
  b) table<u>s</u>
  c) belief<u>s</u>
  d) wish<u>es</u>
  e) box<u>es</u>

3 a) My dad wanted to look around the old <u>churches</u>.
  b) We saw some <u>deer</u> in the forest.
  c) My mum must have at least twenty <u>scarves</u>.
  d) Have you eaten all the <u>cherries</u>?
  e) I love kicking piles of autumn <u>leaves</u>.

4 a) sandwiches
  b) moose
  c) memories
  d) dishes
  e) knives

PREFIXES 1

1 a) I wasn't very impressed with the food. It was a bit <u>over</u>cooked.
  b) That's one of the <u>dis</u>advantages of living in the country.
  c) The match ended in a draw so they will have to <u>re</u>play it.
  d) Unfortunately, I think she <u>mis</u>understood my instructions.

2 I really dislike having to get up in the dark.

   The teacher told her to rewrite the whole essay.

   Sara is definitely underpaid for all that

work she does.

I think David misheard what I said.

3 a) disobey

b) disappear

c) dishonest

d) overcrowded

e) misread

f) misspell

4 Jogging is how I de-stress when I'm feeling overworked.

5 a) In my opinion, Hollywood actors are all overpaid.

b) If children misbehave in class, the teacher tells them off.

c) Isabel doesn't like the colour we painted her bedroom – I think we may have to repaint it.

d) Anyone found breaking the rules will immediately be disqualified from the competition.

PREFIXES 2

1 a) immortal

b) incredible

c) unusual

d) irregular

e) illegal

2 a) im

b) in

c) in

d) in

e) im

3 a) unbelievable

b) impatient

c) irregular

d) unable

e) informal

4 a) illegal

b) unpacked

c) invisible

d) impolite

5 *Possible answers:*

a) Sam had eaten all the food, which was a bit inconsiderate of him.

b) The floor was very uneven.

c) He is very irresponsible.

PREFIXES 3

1 a) So how do you keep warm in sub-zero temperatures?

b) After the concert, I got the lead singer's autograph

c) I can't perform miracles – I'm not superhuman!

2 *Possible answers:*

a) The doors are automatic.

b) My favourite superhero is Iron Man.

HYPHENATING PREFIXES

1 reelect, cooperate, reintroduce, reorder, proactive

2 a) re-elect

b) co-operate

c) re-introduce

d) re-order

e) pro-active

3 a) She first represented her country at the Olympics aged just seventeen.

She was originally given the award last year and then re-presented with it at a later ceremony.

b) I think I might re-sort those cupboards – I'm going to put all the pens in one place and the paper in another.

The shops were all closed so I had to <u>resort</u> to eating last week's stale bread!

c) I wasn't sure whether Ethan got my original email so I <u>re-sent</u> it.

I thought he might <u>resent</u> the fact that his brother got more money than him.

d) We no longer needed the rope so I <u>re-coiled</u> it neatly and left it in the garage.

She <u>recoiled</u> in horror at the sight of the wound.

e) After thirty years working for the same company, he's decided to <u>resign</u>.

I was asked to <u>re-sign</u> the form in black ink this time.

4 a) We hope very much that everyone will <u>co-</u>operate and we can all work together.

b) These animals died out in this region fifty years ago but were recently <u>re-</u>introduced.

c) It's a website that allows you to buy items that have been <u>pre-</u>owned.

d) She was elected leader of the party four years ago and was <u>re-</u>elected last month.

SUFFIXES

1 a) She scrawled her signature (messily) at the end of the letter.

b) Someone had (grabbed) her bag and run off with it.

c) I think we need to (simplify) the instructions for the younger children.

d) Tom is always dropping and spilling things. I've never known such (clumsiness).

e) Emily (begged) me to take her to the fair.

2 b) stopped

c) prettiness

d) preferred

e) sitting

3 modernise

classify

accelerate

4 a) I'd like to apolog<u>ise</u> for making so much noise last night.

b) I've decided to nomin<u>ate</u> Otis to represent our class.

c) We have to categor<u>ise</u> these foods according to their food group.

d) You can see these details when you magn<u>ify</u> the cells under a microscope.

e) I'm going to dedic<u>ate</u> this poem to my sister.

5 In the poem, birds seem to symbolise freedom.

These insects are easy to identify with their red markings.

Dolphins continue to fascinate us with their behaviour.

They seem to communicate using clicks and whistles.

WORDS ENDING IN 'TION', 'SION', 'SSION' AND 'CIAN'

1 a) My sister is doing a lot of revi<u>sion</u> for her exams.

b) In which direc<u>tion</u> did they go?

c) I need to do some calcula<u>tion</u>s.

d) We had to call an electri<u>cian</u> to fix the problem.

e) Jack does a really good impre<u>ssion</u> of Mrs Baker.

2 celebration

musician

admission

extension

3 a) I think you made a good deci<u>sion</u>.

b) 'St.' is an abbrevia<u>tion</u> for 'street'.

c) I have a confe<u>ssion</u> to make.

d) He's a famous poli<u>tici</u>an.

e) Both movies are anima<u>tions</u>.

4

	¹v	e	r	s	i	²o	n				³e	
						p					x	
			⁴a	d	d	i	t	i	o	n	p	
						t					l	
			⁵d	i	s	c	u	s	s	i	o	n
						i					s	
						a					i	
⁶c	a	u	t	i	o	n					o	
											n	

WORDS ENDING IN 'CIOUS' AND 'TIOUS'

1 a) My last bedroom was very small but this one is much more spa<u>cious</u>.

b) It wasn't a mali<u>cious</u> act. She meant no harm.

c) Sweets and cake are very nice, but they're not very nutri<u>tious</u>.

d) Is the disease infec<u>tious</u>?

2 a) superstitious ✓

b) ambitious ✓

c) cautious ✓

d) spacious ✓

WORDS ENDING IN 'CIAL' AND 'TIAL'

1 a) I've never seen such heavy rain. It was absolutely torren<u>tial</u>!

b) If you ride a bicycle, it is cru<u>cial</u> that the brakes work properly.

c) Do you think those flowers are real or artifi<u>cial</u>?

d) He never really liked so<u>cial</u> occasions, such as parties.

e) This will be the President's first offi<u>cial</u> visit.

2

ending in -cial	ending in -tial
beneficial	essential
racial	substantial
	influential
	spatial

WORDS ENDING IN 'ENT' AND 'ANT'

1 a) To my ⟨amazement⟩ I actually won the competition.

b) She's not very ⟨confident⟩ about speaking up in class.

c) The weather was very ⟨pleasant⟩

d) Basic language skills are so ⟨important⟩

e) The ⟨pavements⟩ here are very narrow.

2 a) accid<u>e</u>nt

b) eleph<u>a</u>nt

c) const<u>a</u>nt

d) fragm<u>e</u>nts

3 a) Incorrect

b) Correct

c) Correct

d) Incorrect

e) Correct

4

ending in '-ent'	ending in '-ant'
excellent	defiant
agreement	attendant
obedient	participant
	brilliant

5 a) opponent

b) document

c) obedient

d) permanent

e) comment

6 a) instrum<u>e</u>nt

  b) pres<u>e</u>nt

  c) incid<u>e</u>nt

  d) statem<u>e</u>nt

WORDS ENDING IN 'ANCE', 'ANCY', 'ENCE' AND 'ENCY'

1 frequency

  vacancy

  excellence

  appearance

2 a) He tackled the work with is usual effici<u>ency</u>.

  b) The audi<u>ence</u> clapped loudly when she came on stage

  c) It was a brilliant perform<u>ance</u> by this young actor.

  d) It's such a nuis<u>ance</u> having to go all the way home and collect your kit!

3 a) Incorrect

  b) Correct

  c) Incorrect

  d) Correct

4

							¹s				
				²s		i					
				e		l				³f
	⁴d	i	s	t	a	n	c	e			l
				t		n				u
⁵b	a	l	a	n	c	e		c			e
				n		e				n
				c						c
		⁶e	x	p	e	c	t	a	n	c	y

5 a) violence

  b) presidency

  c) importance

  d) relevance

WORDS ENDING IN 'ABLE', 'IBLE', 'ABLY' AND 'IBLY'

1 a) I'll prob⟨ably⟩ see you at Isabel's house.

  b) She very sens⟨ibly⟩ decided to save her money.

  c) It's going to be cold so make sure you dress suit⟨ably⟩

  d) Lara was vis⟨ibly⟩ upset by his comments.

2 a) capable ✓

  b) horribly ✓

  c) memorable ✓

  d) visible ✓

3 She's a very likable character.

  This is arguably the best café in town.

  The writing is very clear and accessible for children.

  I found the whole film terribly sad.

4 a) There are three syll<u>ables</u> in the word 'terrible'.

  b) I find chocolate irresist<u>ible</u>.

  c) I can't write a whole essay in half an hour – that's imposs<u>ible</u>!

  d) Puppies are just so lov<u>able</u>.

  e) You have to be really flex<u>ible</u> to be a gymnast.

5 a) incredible

  b) inedible

  c) unbearable

6 *Possible answers:*

  a) We need someone reliable to do the work.

  b) I can't possibly finish this essay in ten minutes.

  c) The whole story was unbearably sad.

'EI' AND 'IE'

1 a) receipt

  b) ceiling

  c) thief

  d) field

2 a) piece ✓

  b) receive ✓

  c) brief ✓

  d) relief ✓

3 a) niece

  b) received

  c) friend

  d) piece

4 a) The dog he was holding looked really (fierce)

  b) Her top was pink and her trousers were (beige)

  c) Their standards of (hygiene) are fairly poor.

  d) Are you eating enough (protein)?

  e) Do you know where (their) house is?

5 a) Correct

  b) Incorrect

  c) Correct

  d) Correct

  e) Incorrect

'OUGH' WORDS

1 a) uff

  b) oa/ow

  c) oa/ow

  d) uff

  e) uff

  f) oa/ow

2

oh	uh	or	uff
doughnut	thorough	brought	enough
though		nought	tough
		sought	

3 a) Eva has a sore throat and a bad <u>cough</u>.

  b) You really <u>ought</u> to work a bit harder.

  c) Have you had <u>enough</u> to eat, Tom?

  d) I <u>bought</u> some bread and milk from the supermarket.

SILENT LETTERS AND UNSTRESSED VOWELS

1 a) (w)reck **f)** desi(g)n

  b) (k)nuckle **g)** (k)now

  c) dou(b)t **h)** lim(b)

  d) forei(g)n **i)** (g)naw

  e) fas(t)en **j)** w(h)eel

2 a) reined

  b) nife

  c) weels

  d) climed

  e) whisled

3   present, accident, general, offer

4   petal, hospital, similar, library

5 a) definite

  b) factory

  c) medicine

  d) angrily

  e) freedom

  f) calendar

  g) separate

  h) business

  i) vegetable

  j) chocolate

6 a) frightening

  b) different

  c) reference

  d) general

HOMOPHONES

  a) If you leave your bike there, someone might (steal) it.

  b) This is our house and that's (their) house.

  c) I can't decide which dress to (wear) to the party.

  d) We picked some delicious (pears) from the tree.

  e) Where do I (write) my name?

2 a) The dog wagged her <u>tail</u> happily.

  b) I couldn't wait to <u>meet</u> my new baby sister!

  c) I'll see you next <u>week</u>.

  d) I couldn't <u>accept</u> money from her.

  e) I didn't go to the party. I was just <u>too</u> tired.

3 a) I think I might <u>dye</u> my hair a different colour.

  b) You need to get hold of the plant by its <u>root</u> to pull it up.

  c) We briefly saw a <u>deer</u> in the forest before it ran off.

  d) If they can't find any food, these animals will <u>die</u>.

  e) <u>Dear</u> Anna, I'm writing to invite you to our party!

  f) I'm going to take a different <u>route</u> to college today.

4 a) write

  b) male

  c) been

  d) waste

  e) whether

5 a) bear

  b) flour

  c) knight

  d) pear

  e) steel

SATs PRACTICE

1 You can pre-order the game online.

2 This flower is very special as it symbol(ises) happi(ness) and health.

3 mis- (e.g. misspell) = wrong

  re- (e.g. rejoin) = again

  dis- (e.g. disagree) = not or opposite

  over- (e.g. 'overeat') = too much

SPELLING TASK

1 allergies

2 hungrily

3 official

4 niece

5 Whose

6 Foxes

7 magician

8 You're

9 enough

10 piece

GLOSSARY

abstract noun a noun that refers to feelings, ideas or states that do not exist physically (e.g. 'hope', 'love')

adjective a word used to describe something or somebody (e.g. 'red', 'interesting')

adverb a word that gives information about a verb, adjective or another adverb, sometimes formed by adding 'ly' to an adjective (e.g. 'slowly', 'anxiously')

adverbial a phrase that functions like an adverb

apostrophe (') a punctuation mark that is used to show possession or in contractions

brackets () a pair of punctuation marks used either side of extra information in a sentence

capital letter the form of a letter that is written A, B, C, etc., used at the beginning of a sentence, for example

clause a special phrase that includes a subject and a verb; a clause can be a complete sentence

cohesive device a word such as 'however' or 'moreover', used to link sentences or paragraphs and show the relationship between them

collective noun a noun that is used to refer to a group of things (e.g. 'family', 'team')

comma (,) a punctuation mark that is used to divide clauses or items in a list, for example

command a sentence or phrase that tells someone to do something

common noun an ordinary noun that starts with a lower-case letter (e.g. 'table', 'anger', 'air')

complex sentence a sentence usually made up of a main clause and one or more subordinate clauses

compound sentence a sentence made up of two independent clauses joined by a co-ordinating conjunction

concrete noun a word for things you can detect with your senses (e.g. 'water', 'arm', 'zebra')

conjunction a word that links two words or phrases together; there are two types: co-ordinating conjunctions and subordinating conjunctions

consonant a letter of the alphabet that is not a vowel

contraction (or contracted form) a word that is made by joining two words but omitting a letter or letters (e.g. 'don't', 'I'm')

co-ordinating conjunction a conjunction that links two words or phrases together as an equal pair

dash (–) a punctuation mark used to add extra information in a sentence or to indicate a pause before part of a sentence, for example

determiner a word that specifies a noun as known or unknown (e.g. 'the', 'a', 'this', 'my', 'some')

exclamation a sentence or phrase that begins with 'how' or 'what' and ends with an exclamation mark, used to express strong feelings such as surprise or shock

exclamation mark (!) a punctuation mark that is used at the end of an exclamation

fronted adverbial a word or phrase that acts as an adverb and which goes at the beginning of a sentence (e.g. 'In the end', 'On the other hand')

full stop (.) a punctuation mark that is used at the end of a statement

homophones words that sound the same, but have different spellings and meanings (e.g. 'bear'/'bare')

hyphen a short line used for joining words together (e.g. 'record-breaking', 'flat-screen')

inverted comma one of a pair of marks ' ' or " ", used in written language for showing what someone said (also called *speech marks*)

irregular describing words that do not follow the usual patterns of words of a similar type

main clause part of a sentence with a subject and a verb; a sentence contains at least one main clause, which makes sense on its own

modal verb a verb such as 'can', 'could', 'may', 'shall', that is used with another verb to express, for example, probability, permission, ability, advice and obligation

negative a form of a word that means 'no' or 'not'

non-standard English any form of English that is not accepted as a conventional form

noun a word that is used for a thing, person, place, substance, feeling, etc. (e.g. 'table', 'thought', 'energy', 'London')

noun phrase a phrase with a noun as its main part

paragraph part of a text that usually contains several sentences; each paragraph starts on a new line

parenthesis when extra information is added to a sentence using pairs of brackets, dashes or commas.

past perfect the tense that is used to talk about things that happened before the main action started, formed with 'had' and a past tense verb (e.g. 'They had already arrived')

past progressive the tense we use to talk about things that were happening over a period of time in the past, formed with the verb 'was' or 'were' and an '-ing' verb (e.g. 'I was making bread')

personal pronoun a pronoun that is used to refer to a person or thing (e.g. 'I', 'them', 'it')

phrase a group of words that are grammatically connected

plural a word that shows that you are talking about more than one person or thing (e.g. 'legs', 'churches', 'mice')

possessive pronoun a pronoun that shows who owns something (e.g. 'ours', 'mine', 'yours')

prefix a letter or a group of letters added to the beginning of a word or letters, which alters its meaning (e.g. 'aeroplane', 'illegal')

preposition a word that tells the reader the relationship between things or people (e.g. 'near', 'by', 'under', 'towards')

present perfect the tense that shows past events and uses 'has' or 'have' and a past tense verb (e.g. 'He has gone away')

present progressive the tense we use to talk about things that are happening now, formed with the verb 'be' and an '-ing' verb (e.g. 'I am making bread')

pronoun a word that is used instead of a noun (e.g. 'it', 'they', 'this', 'she', 'mine')

proper noun a name for things like people, places, historical events, organisations, days and months

question a sentence or phrase that asks someone something

question mark (?) a punctuation mark that is used at the end of a question

question tag a short phrase such as 'isn't it?' or 'don't they?' used after a statement to see if someone agrees with you

relative clause part of a sentence beginning with a relative pronoun, which gives extra information about a noun

relative pronoun a word used to link a clause to a noun or pronoun (e.g. 'which', 'that', 'who')

reported speech an account of what has been said, without using the exact words spoken

root word (*or* **root form**) the most basic form of a word

simple past the past tense that is usually formed by adding 'd' or 'ed' to the verb

simple present the present tense that is used for regular events and situations or states that do not change

simple sentence a sentence with one main clause, usually containing a subject, verb and object

speech marks inverted commas

standard English the form of English most widely accepted as the conventional form

statement a sentence that tells you something

subject the person or thing that does the action of a verb

subordinate clause a clause that depends on another clause in order to make sense

subordinating conjunction a conjunction that introduces a subordinate clause

suffix a letter or a group of letters added to the end of a word or letters, which alters its grammatical form (e.g. 'sweet**ness**', 'driv**er**')

tense the way verbs are used to show the time (past, present or future) that the writer is talking about

verb a word that is used to talk about an action or a state (e.g. 'walk', 'happen', 'understand')

vowel one of the letters 'a', 'e', 'i', 'o' or 'u'

word family a group of words that all include a part that is the same or similar, so that the meanings are connected (e.g. 'happy', 'happiness', 'happily')